BOOK 2

CARE
—OF THE—
HORSE

THE BRITISH HORSE SOCIETY

THE MANUAL OF
STABLE MANAGEMENT

The Kenilworth Press Limited

COMPILED BY
Pat Smallwood FBHS

THE ADVISORY PANEL INCLUDED
Barbara Slane Fleming FBHS
Tessa Martin-Bird FBHS
Stewart Hastie MRCVS
Jeremy Houghton-Brown
Helen Webber FBHS
Michael Simons
Dr James L. Duncan
Jane McHugh

SERIES EDITOR
Jane Kidd

Reprinted in enlarged format 1991, 1992

British Library Cataloguing in Publication Data
British Horse Society manual of stable
  management
  Bk.2: Care of the horse
  1. Livestock: Horses. Management
  I. British Horse Society, *Advisory Panel*
  636.1'083

  ISBN 1-872082-18-1

Produced for The British Horse Society by
The Kenilworth Press Limited,
Addington, Buckingham, MK18 2JR

Printed and bound in Great Britain by
Hollen Street Press Ltd, Slough, Berks.

CONTENTS

Introduction

The aim of this series is to provide a reliable source of information and advice on all practical aspects of horse and stable management. Throughout the series emphasis is placed on the adoption of correct and safe procedures for the welfare of all who come into contact with horses, as well for the animals themselves.

The books have been compiled by a panel of experts, each drawing on considerable experience and contributing specialised knowledge on his or her chosen subject.

The other titles in the series are:

Book 1, The Horse – Conformation; Action; Psychology of the Horse; Teeth and Ageing; Breeds; Breeding; Identification; Buying and Selling; Glossary of Terms.

Book 3, The Horse at Grass – Grassland Management; Management of Horses and Ponies at Grass; Working the Grass-kept Pony or Horse; Bringing a Horse up from Grass.

Book 4, Saddlery – Saddles; Bridles; Other Saddlery; Bits; Boots and Bandages; Clothing; Care and Cleaning of Leather; Saddling and Unsaddling.

Book 5, Specialist Care of the Competition Horse Dressage Horse; Driving Horse; Show Jumper; Event Horse; Long-Distance Horse; Hunter; Show Horse or Pony; Point-to-Pointer; Polo Pony; Types of Transportation; Travelling.

Book 6, The Stable Yard – Construction; Riding Schools; Organising and Running a Yard; The Buying of Fodder and Bedding; The Law.

Book 7, Watering and Feeding – Watering; Natural Feeding; The Digestive System; Principles of Feeding; Foodstuffs; Rations; Problem Eaters; The Feed Shed, Storage and Bulk Purchasing.

NOTE: *Throughout the book the term 'horses' is used and it will often include ponies.*

CHAPTER 1
Handling the Horse

In the following pages, advice is given on how to handle, groom and move around a stabled horse. The advice is well tried and proven. When young people are being trained it is essential that they get into the habit of working in a safe way. It is in their own interests and those of the horses to do so. During training they usually look after quiet animals, who are easy to handle, but if correct procedure is practised from the beginning, it will become instinctive to do the right thing, even when they are faced with more difficult animals.

Horses are by nature nervous creatures. Most become docile and quiet if they are well handled; others always remain on edge and require quiet, confident handling. The expression in the horse's eye will indicate his state of mind, revealing whether he is calm and relaxed, or worried and frightened. A worried, frightened horse must always be treated with care. He requires firm but kind handling if he is not to become a danger both to himself and to his attendants.

Horses have to be taught good stable manners and behaviour. Well-trained grooms are able to do this. They are also capable of advising and helping other less experienced staff. Horses are creatures of habit, and they become more relaxed if there is a routine to their life.

Horses respond to the tone of a voice, and in this way they can be rewarded for good behaviour, or corrected for bad behaviour. When entering the stable, always speak first. Go up to the horse's shoulder and pat him on the neck. Before handling him further, put on a headcollar and tie him up with a quick-release knot (see diagram). He should be tied up sufficiently short to prevent him turning and nipping or biting, but not so short that he feels constrained, is frightened and pulls back.

When dealing with the legs and feet, never kneel or sit, always crouch. If they are frightened or worried, some horses will use their legs as defence and they may:

Strike out with the front feet – so when holding a horse always stand to the side and never in front.

Deliver a cow kick with a hind foot.

Kick forward and out to the side.

Kick out to the back with one or both hind feet.

To minimise the danger of being kicked, never stand behind the horse. When attending to legs or feet, always stand close to the horse. Doing so minimises the impact of any kicks.

SECURING THE HORSE

In a Stable
Horses should always be tied up when a groom is either working in the stable or actually grooming. They should wear a headcollar; the rope or chain should be attached to the back of the headcollar and thence tied to the string loop on the tie-up ring with a quick-release knot (see diagram opposite). The purpose of the string loop is that it will break if the horse pulls back violently. It is important therefore to use string that will break under stress.

In a Stall
Horses kept in stalls are tied up by means of a headcollar, a clip-on rope and a log. This method allows them sufficient

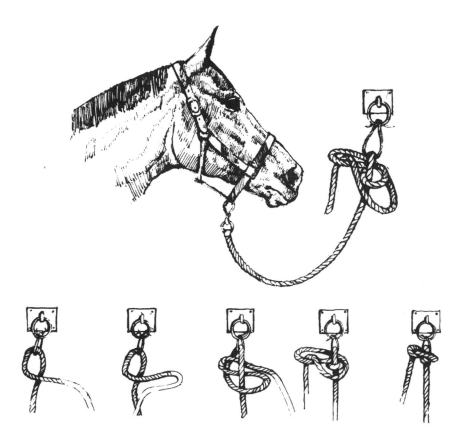

Quick-release knot.

room to lie down, but the heavy log takes up the slack of the rope, so that there is no danger of the horse getting his foot caught. The log is a piece of heavy wood (preferably circular), with a hole drilled through the middle large enough to take the rope. The headcollar rope is passed through a ring or an opening in the fixed manger, and is then fastened to the log by means of a slip knot. This is made to lie across the base of the hole, so that it cannot pull through. Straw placed in this knot will prevent it pulling too tight and becoming difficult to undo. An alternative is to put a short length of twisted string through the log and secure the rope to this. A tie-up ring and string loop above the manger give a shorter tie-up when the horse is being groomed.

9

Handling the Horse

PICKING UP THE FEET

To pick up the near fore, stand by the near-side shoulder, facing the tail. Pat the neck, run the hand down the shoulder and leg to the fetlock joint, squeeze above the joint, and at the same time slightly push the horse over with the shoulder so that he puts weight on the off fore. When not picking out the feet, face the horse's shoulder, support the weight of the horse's foot by placing the toe of the foot in the palm of the right hand, and hold it with the fingers. When picking out the feet, face the rear, hold the foot in the left hand, and use the hoof pick in the right hand. The process is reversed for the off fore.

To pick up a hind foot, either of the following methods may be used, but the first is safer if the horse is likely to kick:

(1) Face the tail and pat the neck. When picking up the near hind, run the left hand along the body, quarters, and down the back and outside of the hind leg. Squeeze the fetlock, and ease the leg a little forward and up. Keep an arm between the face and the horse's leg. When not picking out the foot, use the right hand to support the foot; slip the left hand round to the front of the leg, and hold the foot in the palm. Do not hold the toe high, as this will unbalance the horse. When picking out the foot, take up the foot as above, then hold it in the left hand. Allow the horse's leg to move to the rear, and pick out with the right hand.

(2) Slide the left hand around the inner side of the hock, and run it down the fetlock. Pick up the foot as before.

Never leave the arm supporting the hind leg behind the horse as a sudden kick may result in its being broken.

GROOMING

Sensitive horses, particularly when fit, are often tricky to groom. They require firm but tactful handling. Corrections can be given by the voice or a slap, but only in exceptional circumstances should a horse be hit, and never by junior or inexperienced staff, who are liable to punish the horse at the wrong moment for the wrong reason. Rough handling of horses in the stable is a sign of bad temper or nerves on the part of the groom, and can only have a bad effect on the horse.

When being groomed, horses may bite through irritation, discomfort or over-freshness. Should this occur:

☐ A muzzle may be put over the headcollar and the horse tied up in the usual way.

☐ The rope can be put through the stable ring and held with one hand while the other uses the brush. In this way, the horse is kept under control.

RESTRAINT

Restraint is most likely to succeed if it is applied in a kind but firm manner by a person whom the horse knows and respects. Additional aids:

☐ Fidgety horses often stand if they are given a small feed or are fed by hand with sliced carrots or apples.

☐ If treatment allows, an attendant can hold up a front leg.

Holding up the front leg
for restraint.

11

Handling the Horse

☐ The horse's attention can be distracted by:
  Patting him on the neck.
  Scratching him between the jaw bones, under his throat and round his ears.
  Gripping loose skin on his neck.

☐ A cavesson headcollar or a snaffle bridle gives more control than a stable headcollar. Care must be taken that the handler does not attempt to restrain the horse by jerking the reins of the bridle and thus damaging his mouth.

☐ Holding an ear or the upper lip in the fingers can be effective. It makes a mild form of twitch. Take care not to interfere with the breathing.

☐ If the above are not successful, a twitch is the quickest and least traumatic means of restraint for most horses. This can be made using a piece of smoothly finished wood about 46cm (18in) long (a broken-off hay fork handle, well planed down, is ideal). A hole is drilled in

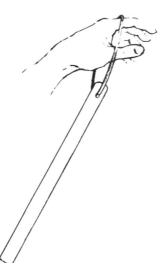

Twitch with cord over fingers ready to put on.

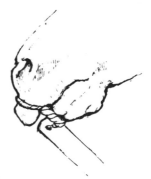

Twitch in position.

one end, through which is threaded 30cm (12in) of soft thick cord made into a loop. Thin string must not be used, as it is likely to cut into the horse's nose.

Various forms of patented twitches are available. One type takes the form of two metal handles hinged together at the top. The device is placed on the horse's upper lip and held firm by squeezing together the bottom of the handles. The main asset of this type of twitch is its quick release, but it is more difficult to keep in place should the horse resist.

Recent investigation has revealed that the twitch, which formerly was thought to achieve its restraining and quietening effect as a result of the pain inflicted on the nose, works in a quite different way. Once the twitch has been placed on the nose and the horse has submitted to it, sensory stimulation of muzzle reflexes releases pain-killing agents called endorphins into the bloodstream. These have an analgesic effect so that the horse becomes quiet and less aware of pain and other stimuli.

A twitch should never be placed on a horse's ear. Do not hold the horse by the twitch alone and never leave it on for more than 15 to 20 minutes.

Putting on a cord twitch

An assistant should hold the horse. The handler takes the end of the twitch in one hand and places the other hand through the loop of cord. He then grips the horse's upper lip with this hand, slips the loop over the horse's lip and twists the end of the handle until the cord is tight. The twitch should then be held at the end of the handle. This is the easiest way to hold it securely.

When the twitch is released, the horse's upper lip should be firmly rubbed to help restore circulation. A twitch left on too long can cause a permanent scar.

Some horses become adept at getting out of a twitch, particularly if the handler, in an effort to be kind, has failed to put it on sufficiently tightly. They can then often be difficult to re-twitch.

Most horses accept the twitch, and their treatment can

Horse with twitch being held for treatment.

be concluded without any more trouble. However, certain horses become violent and dangerous; such animals should never be twitched.

It is possible for one person to put on a twitch and to secure it by tying the handle to the headcollar. However, this is a dangerous procedure, as the twitch can become loose, the horse may then throw his head about, and the handle of the twitch may injure both horse and handler.

If other methods of restraint fail, it may be necessary to sedate or anaesthetise the animal (see *Clipping*, page 71).

Attending to the Mouth or Teeth

Some veterinary surgeons use a gag, which is a device placed on the horse's lower face and adjusted to hold his jaws apart so that his teeth can be reached for rasping, scaling or the removal of wolf teeth. When attending to or examining the mouth and teeth it is often necessary to hold the tongue and bring it out to the side of the mouth. Care should be taken that the tongue is not injured by pulling or twisting, or the use of unnecessary strength. If the horse struggles, let go of the tongue immediately.

Never pass the tongue from one side of the mouth to

14

the other. Let it go and re-take it from the other side. If the tongue is pulled out to the front, there is a danger of the incisor teeth cutting into it. If it is pulled out and backwards, the upper first molar may cut it.

ADMINISTERING MEDICINES AND POWDERS

By Syringe
Large, used, well-cleaned, wormer syringes are suitable. Most powders can be mixed with water, placed in the syringe and squirted down the horse's throat. This is the most efficient method of dosing the horse, other than by injection or stomach tube. The syringe is placed in the corner of the horse's mouth, pointing down over the tongue, and firmly squirted. The horse's muzzle can then be raised to assist swallowing. Should any liquid remain in the horse's mouth, food should not be allowed for several minutes.

In Food
Powders can be mixed with a damp feed. Soaked sugar beet or molasses help to disguise the taste. Take care not to spoil the horse's appetite by using this method.

Examining teeth.

15

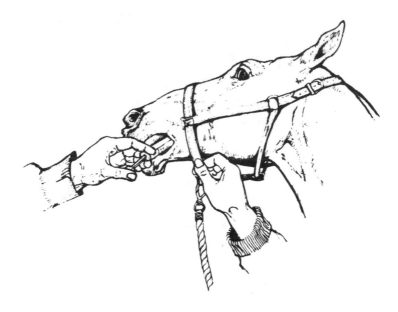

Worming or administering medicine.

In Water
Certain soluble medicines can be given in the drinking water. Care should be taken that the horse is not put off drinking, as this could cause other problems.

As an Electuary
The powder is mixed with treacle or honey and is placed on the horse's tongue with a smooth piece of wood or a wooden spoon.

Drenching
Large doses of liquid medicine can be given by drench. Efficient drenching requires skill and practice. Inexperienced administration can cause choking and death. Horses with respiratory problems should never be drenched. Modern veterinary practice is generally not in favour of this method.

By Stomach Tube
This method should only be used by a veterinary surgeon.

By Injection
Intra-muscular injections, if authorised by a veterinary surgeon, may be given by an experienced horse owner or trained groom. To give an injection efficiently requires practice and skill. *Intra-venous* injections should only be given by a qualified veterinary surgeon.

It must be the responsibility of the stable manager to ensure that difficult horses are handled only by experienced people. If they are mishandled by nervous or inexperienced staff, they may at best become playful, and at worst cause an accident. Consult the *Health and Safety at Work* regulations.

Protection of the Knee or Leg after Treatment
Horses often attempt to chew at a knee covering, especially one applied over a wound. Preventive measures include:

Side reins from the roller to the headcollar. The nosepiece of the headcollar should be lined with Gamgee or sheepskin to prevent rubbing. The side reins are fixed to the side squares, and then attached to the roller. The horse will need to be watered and fed at a suitable height.

A cradle. This is a framework of wood which is placed on the horse's neck, and prevents him putting his head down. It is secured with leather straps. The crest and withers should be protected with a pad.

A knee cap will sometimes solve the problem if protection only is required for the knee.

LEADING THE HORSE IN HAND

A horse is normally led from the near side, except when on a road. He should, however, be taught to lead equally well from both sides.

17

In a Headcollar
Put on the headcollar and rope or halter. Tie a knot in the
end of the rope. Hold the end of the rope in the left hand,
but never wrap the rope around the hand. Put the right hand
on the rope, about 30cm (12ins) from the horse's head. With
a fresh horse, put the hand over the top of the rope to help
restrain him. With a lazy horse, put the hand under the rope
to help push him forward. Never attempt to go ahead of the
horse and try to pull him along, as his reaction will then be
to pull back. The person leading should always be by the
horse's shoulder, never in front; he should look ahead, not
at the horse.

In the case of a fresh or strange horse, it is advisable to
lead the horse from a cavesson headcollar with a lunge rein
or long rope attached. Horses should never be led from a
headcollar without a lead rope. If the horse plays up it will
be impossible to hold him and the leader may injure an arm
or hand.

When on foot and leading a young or fresh horse, gloves
should be worn. These give a safer grip and prevent rein
or rope scalds, which could result in a dropped rein and a
loose horse. Such animals may well rear in play, and since
the head of the leader is vulnerable, it is advisable to wear
a hard hat. Strong leather boots or shoes are recommended,
to give extra protection to the feet, should the horse jump or
tread on them.

In a Bridle
Take the reins of the bridle over the head, and hold
them in the right hand, with the end of the reins in the
left hand, as for a rope, but with the reins separated by the
first finger. The stick is carried in the left hand, pointing to
the rear. If the horse is lazy, the left hand should be moved
back behind the body and the horse tapped on the lower rib
cage, just to the rear of where a rider's leg would rest.

In a Saddle and Bridle
Ensure that the stirrups are run up and secured, as they

18

are for lungeing. The girths should be done up, but not too tightly. A running martingale should be detached from the reins and secured to the neck strap. Then proceed as above. The point of the stirrup bars may be turned up to give extra security to the leathers. These points should never be turned up when the horse is being ridden.

Leading the Horse on a Road
Ponies when brought in from the field to the stable may be led back in halters or headcollars. However, if it is known that a pony is difficult to control, or is traffic shy, he should be led in a cavesson or bridle. If a horse has to be led along a main road, a bridle should always be used for safety and to fulfil insurance requirements in the case of an accident. The person leading the horse should be between the horse and the traffic and on the left-hand side of the road.

Horses Being Led Out for Exercise
Whether beside another horse or on foot, horses should wear a snaffle bridle or cavesson. They should be led in the direction of the flow or traffic with the led horse on the inside of the leader, whether the latter is on a horse or on foot. The near-side rein of the bridle can be put through the ring to the bit on the off side, and then both reins should be held with the left hand on top of the rein about 5cm (2ins) from the horse's head. The slack of the rein may be held in the right hand.

The reins of the ridden horse should be held in the right hand. The led horse's head should be kept level with the rider's knee. If the led horse is allowed to move too far forward, or too far behind, he becomes more difficult to control. A cavesson with a short lunge rein attached may be used. The reins of the bridle can be crossed and then doubled back over the horse's head. This keeps them out of the way, and makes the horse more comfortable. Alternatively they can, if long enough, be placed behind the stirrups. This is not recommended for young or sensitive horses.

Leading a Horse in and out of a Loosebox or Through Doorways

Because the horse is wider across the hips than the shoulders, it is very easy for him, when led by a careless attendant, to knock and bruise his off-side hip on a doorway. After such a mishap he will be nervous and will try to hurry or rush through doorways, thus risking a repeat injury. In bad cases, a fragment of bone can be displaced. It is important when leading a horse in and out of a loosebox to ensure that:

☐ The horse is securely held and steadied as he reaches the doorway and goes through.

☐ The horse walks on a straight track through the doorway and into the box and does not approach it at an angle.

☐ The groom checks that the door will not swing to and hit the horse as he goes through. On windy days, doors should be hooked open.

☐ The horse is not allowed to go into the box on his own, with the reins thrown over his neck. This will tend to make him hurry.

Trotting out for Soundness

This is best done with the horse wearing a headcollar and no saddle. If the horse is fresh, put on a cavesson headcollar for greater control, and if this is not available, use a snaffle bridle. Check that the yard gate is shut. Trot the horse out slowly, and make allowance for the fact that a cambered yard or corner makes many older horses go unlevel.

To turn the horse, steady him to a walk and push him away from you and round to the right. This gives greater control and the horse stays better balanced and is less likely to step on the leader's foot. If he is allowed to come round to the left, his quarters will tend to swing out, and he may well kick.

Standing up the Horse for Inspection

For inspection or show, square the horse up and show the near side. The front legs should be level, but the near hind should be a little to the rear of the off hind, not vice versa. The attendant stands at the front, but a little to the side of the horse, with the left hand holding the reins, divided by the fingers, about 30cm (12in) from the horse's head. The slack of rein, and the stick, if one is carried, are held in the right hand. To trot the horse up, reverse the hand hold on the reins and stick, and proceed as for leading in a saddle and bridle.

SAFETY PRECAUTIONS

☐ Never lead the horse out of a stable with the rug undone at the front, and wearing a roller with no breastplate. The rug and roller may slip back and frighten the horse, who may then play up and get away.

☐ Always tie the horse up when working in the stable or grooming.

☐ In the case of horses who tend to play with their stable-door bolt and open the door, fit a horse-proof bolt, or at least a spring clip on the bolt.

☐ When tying up a horse outside the box, make sure that he cannot touch or sniff at another horse, as this will cause squealing and possibly kicking. If two or more horses are tied outside, make sure that they are not within sniffing or kicking distance of each other.

☐ Playful horses, who are likely to chew wood or string, or to pull at stable fixtures, should have their stable checked for likely hazards. If necessary, move the horse to a more suitable box.

☐ Yard gates leading to public roads should be kept closed.

Handling the Horse

☐ Should a horse slip up and not be able to rise easily, lean your knee on his head and neck to keep him still. Straw, manure, sacks or old rugs spread on the ground will help,him to get to his feet.

☐ Keep a sharp knife in a predetermined, accessible place in the stable yard. Should a horse become tangled up in a rope, or if he pulls back and is held fast because the safety string fails to break, rapid action will be essential to prevent injury.

CHAPTER 2
Stable Vices and Problem Behaviour

Most stable vices may be classed as nervous habits. They are acquired by the horse as a result of stress or boredom, or by imitation. The tendency may be inherited, that is it may be a question of temperament, but it can often be avoided through good stable management and firm but considerate handling of the horse.

The following measures help to relieve stress and to avoid boredom:

- For feeding, grooming, exercise and stables a regular timetable should be adhered to.

- Sufficient bulk food should be provided to occupy the horse when he is in his loosebox. Many nervous habits start when horses in training have their hay reduced.

- Extra care must be taken with a horse who is on complete nuts and reduced bulk. A lump of rock salt should be put in his loosebox. To prevent chewing of wooden stabling, place a length of tree branch in the stable and allow the horse to bark it.

- Since most horses like music, transistor radios played quietly are acceptable items in the stables.

- Because travelling can cause stress, whenever possible

long journeys should be avoided. Never drive too fast, or travel a horse in a noisy trailer.

● Avoid subjecting the horse to undue pressure during training, by either the trainer or the rider asking too much.

VICES

WEAVING

This is a nervous habit most common among well-bred horses. The animal rocks himself to and fro, the head swinging with the movement. Confirmed cases lift each foot in turn as the forehand is swayed from side to side. As a result, extra strain is placed on the tendons of the front legs, and lameness can occur. Established weavers give themselves little rest, and often lose condition. The habit is catching, being quickly imitated by other horses. Animals sometimes continue the habit even when they are tied up in a loosebox or stabled in a stall. In the latter case, if they are turned round and put on pillar chains (chains or ropes attached to the rear side pillars of the stalls and then hooked to the headcollar), they may become less bored and so lose the habit. Some horses weave when they are first brought up from the field; others only when they become fit and are competing or racing. Some start weaving when they are stabled on their own, others when they are in a line of boxes. There are no fixed rules or indications; each animal reacts in his own particular way.

Remedies

☐ Try to find out the cause, and deal with this side of the problem. A confirmed weaver is incurable, but if a young horse is caught in time, the habit may be checked.

☐ Fix an anti-weaving grid to the top of the lower door of

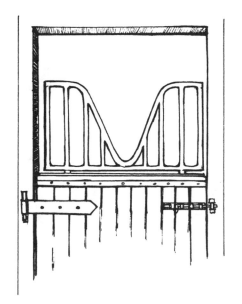

Anti-weaving grid.

the loosebox. This allows the horse to put out his head, but prevents him moving from side to side. Some yards have these grids fitted on all doors to discourage horses from starting the habit.

☐ Alternatively, fix a grille to the top of the lower door to prevent him putting his head out. But bear in mind that although this prevents a horse weaving over the door, boredom may still lead him to continue the habit while standing back in his box.

☐ Take a length of wood, slip the top half through the handle of a rubber dustbin lid and bolt the bottom half firmly to the door. This cheap, easy-to-make device allows the horse to put his head out over the door, but prevents him weaving.

CRIB BITING AND WINDSUCKING

The original cause is usually boredom, though both habits can also be developed by one horse watching another. In

25

crib biting, the horse seizes hold of any projecting edge or object with his teeth, arches his neck and gulps down air. In doing so, he makes a distinctive grunt. When windsucking, the horse does not seize anything with his teeth, but gulps air in a similar manner. A crib biter placed in a loosebox with no suitable surfaces to seize often turns to windsucking.

Crib biters often continue the habit when turned out to grass. The top of fence posts and gates make convenient surfaces. Other mature horses turned out in the same field rarely develop the habit, but young animals may easily do so.

Crib biting.

Windsucking.

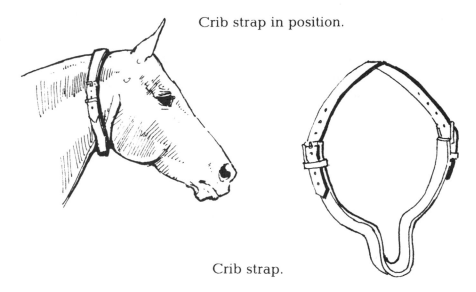

Crib strap in position.

Crib strap.

There appears to be no infallible remedy for these two habits. Numerous preventive measures can be tried. In some cases they may work, but in others they are only successful until the horse learns to outwit the prevention. If caught in the early stages and if no suitable surface is made available, a crib biter sometimes loses the desire and hence the habit.

To prevent crib biting, the loosebox should have no projecting surfaces. A metal grille fitted to the door allows the horse to look out but protects the top of the door from his teeth. It must be sufficiently fine that he cannot seize hold of it.

Should a suitable box not be available, a muzzle is an effective deterrent. The horse should wear it at all times in the stable, except of course when he is being watered or fed or having his hay.

There are various patterns of anti-crib biting straps, of which the Meyers pattern is probably the best. It is made of vulcanite and has a leather strap which runs over the poll and fastens to the headcollar. The vulcanite section has a V-shaped part, which fits tightly up into the gullet, and prevents the horse arching his neck (see diagram). The Matthew Harvey Grinder's Bit is also reputed to stop horses crib biting. When it is removed they do not resume the habit.

A flute bit may be used, fixed to the headcollar. This has a perforated hollow mouthpiece which disperses the gulp of air and prevents it being sucked in.

In recent years, a surgical operation on the neck was at first thought to be effective, but this has since proved less successful.

Weaving, crib biting and windsucking are all stable vices. They must be declared at the time of sale, and should be noted on the veterinary certificate. If this information is withheld, the sale can be declared null and void.

PROBLEM BEHAVIOUR

RUG TEARING

Remedies

The skin and mane should be checked for skin infection and/or parasites. If present, these should be dealt with. This habit is often caused by boredom, and the provision of toys, such as a ball in a haynet or plastic bottles hanging on pieces of string, often helps. A bib of strong leather fastened to the back and side squares of the headcollar, so that it lies behind and below the chin, checks most offenders. Those who persist can be muzzled. A bar muzzle, which allows the horse to pick at hay, is the best type.

KICKING THE STABLE WALLS

This sometimes starts when mares become irritated by the presence of a neighbouring horse. It can also be a sign of ovary trouble in a mare. Moving the horse to a different box may help. Some horses do it only when they are stabled on their own, others only when they are stabled in company.

Anti-rug tearer.

Rats or mice in the stable can also start the habit, or it may be a sign of frustration. The noise seems to be addictive.

Remedies

☐ Line the box with rubber matting.

☐ Hang a sack of straw from the roof, so that it rests just behind the horse's hindquarters.

☐ Hang a bunch of gorse or a broom head in the same position as a sack of straw – although the horse may eat it.

☐ Fit kicking hobbles – though these may cause other problems.

Try to arrange for the horse to spend several hours in the field each day.

BANGING THE STABLE DOOR

This is an irritating habit, which can quickly spread round a yard if it is not checked. It is usually started by horses impatient for feed, particularly if some are fed and others are kept waiting. However, it can become addictive, and horses will bang doors with a front foot or knee as a nervous habit. It can cause bruising and concussion.

Remedies

☐ Fix a grille over the door, so that the horse is kept back and is unable to reach the door with his foot or knee.

☐ Fix an iron bar or a chain across the doorway, so that the door can be left open in working hours. This is usually successful, as long as the arrangements are secure.

☐ If it is essential for the door to be kept closed, set a bar at an angle across the doorway. This will also keep the horse back from the door.

☐ Because many horses appear to enjoy the noise, fix thick matting or lining on the door. This will muffle the noise and may discourage the horse from persisting with the habit.

GNAWING WOOD

Remedies

☐ Apply creosote, or some other strong-flavoured mixture, to wooden stabling.

☐ Cap all accessible surfaces with metal.

☐ Check the fibre and mineral content of the horse's food because in some cases it can be a diet problem.

EATING DROPPINGS

This is usually considered to start as a diet problem, but it can become an addiction.

Remedies

☐ Check the mineral and vitamin content of the horse's diet and correct any deficiencies.

☐ Put a forkful of turf, with roots and earth attached, in the box.

☐ Worm the horse regularly. Seek veterinary advice on a suitable programme of worming and diet supplementation.

EATING STRAW BEDDING

Most horses bedded on straw eat a certain amount of it, but a greedy horse eats so much that it impairs his condition and wind.

Remedies

☐ Bed the horse on shavings, sawdust or paper. Although the shavings and paper may still be chewed, as long as not to excess, they will do no harm.

☐ If straw bedding has to be used, spray it with strong disinfectant. This may deter the horse, but it can also blister the coat of a thin-skinned animal.

PAWING THE GROUND AND STAMPING

The attraction of this habit appears to be the noise which it creates, but it can also be a sign of internal discomfort and/or pain. Heavy, solid rubber matting put down at the front of the loosebox by the door can help to check it. The concrete flooring underneath will sweat, so it should be swept daily and, when possible, exposed to the air.

BITING

Horses who bite when being handled and groomed can be controlled by a muzzle, or by being tied up to two rings across the corner of the box. The cause may be rough grooming – some horses are very sensitive – poor handling when young, or the feeding of tit-bits.

TAIL RUBBING

A horse may rub his tail, either because of the presence of whip worms in the area of the anus and rectum or, in summer, because of sweet itch caused by midges.

Remedies

☐ If the tail rubbing is caused by worms, the horse should be dosed with an appropriate wormer. Keep the area around and under the tail clean, and the tail itself regularly shampooed.

☐ If the cause is sweet itch, a special lotion should be applied. Seek veterinary assistance.

REFUSAL TO LIE DOWN

This puts extra and unnecessary strain on the legs. It is usually caused by one of the following:

Insufficient bedding.

Getting cast.

Slipping when getting up.

Worry in a new stable, especially if there are no other horses.

Remedies

☐ Put the horse on a deep shavings bed or, if straw is used, adopt the deep litter system.

☐ Provide a pony or donkey in a neighbouring field or loosebox for company. This often helps.

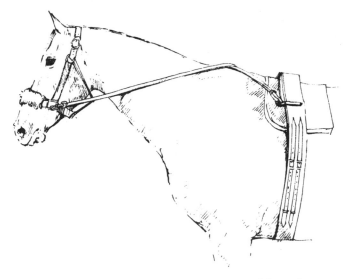

Side reins fitted to prevent tearing of bandages.

Once the horse has overcome his nervousness and has lain down, providing the above precautions are taken, the problem should not recur.

TEARING BANDAGES

A muzzle, cradle or crossed side reins (see also Chapter 1, page 17) are the most effective remedies for this.

PULLING BACK WHEN TIED UP

This habit arises from fright. It usually starts because the horse, when first tied up in a stable, possibly with too short a rope, pulled back and frightened himself. Therefore, always attach a safety loop of string to the ring and tie the rope to the string, never to the ring itself. Unfortunately, once learned, this habit is difficult to cure, and many remedies have attendant risks. Careful handling in the stable may eventually effect a cure. When grooming, try threading the rope through the ring, but not actually tying it. The problem often arises when a horse is being tied up in a trailer if he is allowed to pull back before the back strap is done up, or before the back of the trailer is closed.

HALTER AND HEADCOLLAR SLIPPING

This habit is often acquired as a result of pulling back, tilting the head and learning that the halter or headcollar slips off. Ponies and cobs can be checked by being tied up with thick neck straps instead of a headcollar. This is not wise with young or highly strung horses, as they may pull back, lose their footing, and give themselves a fright and, often, an injury. Such horses should never be left on their own when they are tied up. If they are not allowed to persist in the habit, they may in time forget it.

PROBLEMS IN THE STABLE

CHOKING

Choking results when there is a blockage of the tube down which food passes from the mouth to the stomach. The obstruction can usually be felt by examining the left and lower side of the neck.

Possible Causes

An apple or a large piece of root fed whole and not chopped.

A greedy horse bolting his food.

A tired horse who is suffering from mild dehydration and whose mouth is not salivating.

Feeding certain foodstuffs dry, when they should have been soaked.

The symptoms are salivation and frequent attempts at swallowing, which causes a gurgling sound. The head is either drawn in tight to the chest, or stretched out towards the ground. The neck muscles are tense. There may be a discharge from the nose. The symptoms are alarming.

Treatment

☐ Do not give water.

☐ Do not try to drench the horse.

☐ Smear a lump of butter on the tongue. It may help to ease the obstruction.

☐ Lightly massage the left-hand side of the jugular groove.

Stay with the horse. If he can relax the spasm, the obstruction may move on down. Should the condition not be relieved within half an hour, seek veterinary help.

Horses who are known to bolt their food, particularly cubes, should have their feed mixed with bran or chaff. An alternative is to soak the cubes before feeding, and then feed them mixed with soaked sugar beet.

A CAST HORSE

If a horse rolls over too close to the wall of his loosebox and has insufficient room in which to right himself, he may become cast. Many horses become very frightened and/or violent, and by kicking and struggling do themselves injury. Other more placid horses lie quietly until help arrives. Horses often become cast at night. The tell-tale signs in the morning are a disturbed bed and scratch marks on the wall. This shows that horses, given time, often right themselves without help. If a horse has been cast, he must be closely examined for injury, and then walked out and trotted up in hand.

Horses may roll in their box at any time, but are more likely to do so:

When clean bedding has been added.

When first put back in after work.

When they feel the onset of an attack of colic.

The sight of a cast horse is alarming. As he tries to right himself, his thrashing hooves put a helper at risk. The task should not be attempted by inexperienced persons.

Anti-cast ridges or grooves, which help a cast horse to right himself, can be placed on loosebox walls. His hind feet will catch on the ledge, and he can then push himself over.

Methods of Getting a Horse Up

One person on his own may well be able to right a pony or lightweight animal under 15hh. Considerable strength is required to right a large animal, and two or three people are required, particularly if the horse is very violent.

One person on his own restrains the horse by sitting or kneeling on his head. Make sure his nostril is free. A cloth

Pulling round a cast horse.

placed beneath his head will help prevent damage to the eye on the underside. Reassure the horse with voice and hand, and consider the situation. Sometimes the horse will remain quiet and in a few minutes is able to right himself. If he does not, stand up and release his head. Remove any ridges of bedding immediately behind his back and shoulders. Then take hold of his tail and pull his quarters round. The horse will slightly pivot on his middle and shoulders, which should give him room to extend his legs and get up without trouble.

Two or three people. Collect one or two strong ropes or webbing lunge lines. One assistant sits on the horse's head as before, and the second removes the bedding from behind the horse. Most experienced people fasten the ropes round the front and hind legs nearest the wall using a slip knot. The first assistant releases the horse's head and is then ready to help pull. By pulling on the ropes the horse can be rolled over. He is then able to stand up. Release the ropes as soon as possible.

Righting a horse with ropes.

CHAPTER 3
Grooming

To maintain his health, the stabled horse requires regular daily grooming. The fit horse on a high concentrate diet excretes a considerable amount of waste product through the skin, so thorough grooming is essential. However, there are circumstances when grooming should be reduced. The sick horse, who has to be kept quiet, needs only minimal grooming, while one with an infectious disease, for example ringworm, should not be groomed, since there is a risk of spreading the infection over the horse's body.

When not in work, the grass-kept horse does not require grooming. The natural oils in his coat help to keep him warm. When in work, he requires only modified grooming: remove surface mud, check his feet and generally tidy him up.

Objectives of Grooming

To keep the skin in good condition by removing dirt, sweat and waste products.

To stimulate the circulation of the blood and to tone up muscle.

To improve the horse's appearance.

To provide an opportunity to check for signs of heat or swelling in the legs, soreness in the saddle, girth or mouth areas, heat in the foot, or skin infections.

GROOMING EQUIPMENT AND ITS USES

☐ Container for holding equipment.

☐ Hoof pick for picking out the feet. This should have a length of coloured knotted string attached so that it can easily be seen if it is dropped in the horse's bed.

☐ Rubber curry comb for removing mud and sweat (see *water brush*). It is also used to massage the horse, and to remove loose hairs when a stabled horse is changing his coat.

☐ Dandy brush. This can be used on the coat of unclipped or coarse-coated horses to remove mud and sweat. It should not be used on a thin-coated, sensitive horse.

☐ Body brush for cleaning the coat and for brushing out the mane and tail.

☐ Metal curry comb for cleaning the body brush. It should not be used on the horse.

☐ Hay wisp or leather pad filled with hay, for stimulating the circulation and improving muscle tone.

☐ Sponge for cleaning the eyes, nose, mouth and dock area.

☐ Water brush for laying the mane and damping down the tail. A dry water brush is also useful for removing mud or sweat from thin-skinned horses.

☐ Old dandy brush for washing the feet.

☐ Stable rubber for removing surplus dust and giving a final polish to the coat.

☐ Hoof oil and brush for oiling the feet.

☐ Plastic curry comb, for use on the long-coated or unclipped horse to remove mud and sweat. It can also be used on a thick mane.

All brushes and curry combs should fit the hand of

the groom; the retaining straps should be adjusted as required.

Extra Equipment

☐ Spare stable rubber.

☐ Cactus cloth, a rough, coarse-weave cloth imported from Mexico. It is a very useful addition to grooming equipment for removing dried mud and sweat in place of a rubber curry comb.

☐ Large sponge for use in washing the horse down and removing stable stains.

☐ Sweat scraper, preferably rubber or plastic, to be used to remove surplus water after washing the horse down.

☐ Rubber glove with soft bristles for use when washing down.

☐ Towels for drying off the horse.

☐ Tail comb for pulling the mane and tail and for plaiting.

☐ Mane comb to comb out the mane (this is rarely required).

NB: Neither comb should be used to comb out the tail, as they may break the hairs.

☐ Pair of blunt-ended scissors.

☐ Tail bandage.

METHODS OF GROOMING

Quartering or Brushing Off

This is done in the morning before exercise. If the horse is not to be saddled immediately, the rugs should be left on and simply turned back to allow stable stains to be removed.

Method

☐ Pick out the feet.

☐ Brush off any stable stains. If necessary, wash clean and towel dry. Pay particular attention to the hocks, knees and flank, and under the stomach.

☐ Sponge the eyes, nose and dock.

☐ Brush out the mane and tail.

Strapping

This involves a thorough grooming of the horse, as described below, but in addition he is wisped or banged for 10 to 15 minutes to stimulate circulation of the blood and muscle tone.

In many yards strapping is no longer practised. Each horse is groomed for approximately 20 minutes, or for as long as it takes to get him clean. The procedure is the same as for strapping, but the wisping or banging is omitted. It is felt that balanced feeding and correct work will build up muscle where it is needed, and that the time formerly spent wisping a horse can be better occupied.

Wisp Over

Competition or racehorses are often wisped over again before their tea-time feed, when rugs are checked and the box set fair. This unsettles some sensitive horses, so it is often better to finish the grooming in one session.

The time taken to groom a horse is not necessarily the criterion of expert work. The appearance and feel of the horse must be the final factor when assessing the quality of the work done. An experienced worker should groom his horse in half an hour. After hunting or competing in muddy conditions, it may well take longer. Extra wisping may take 20 minutes.

Grooming

This is the thorough grooming best carried out after

exercise, when the horse is warm and the pores of the skin are open. On hunting or competition days, it is done in the morning instead of quartering. The time taken is 20 to 30 minutes. Wisping or banging is not carried out.

Method
The horse should be dry and cool.

☐ Collect the headcollar and rope (never use a frayed or worn rope as it can tighten and prove impossible to undo), and a bucket of water. A horse who chews his rope can be tied up with a rack chain attached to string, or with a rope soaked in creosote.

☐ Put on the headcollar. Place the rope through a short length of string (called a safety loop), and put that through the stable ring. Tie the rope with a quick-release knot, tucking the end of the rope through the loop, so that the horse cannot pull it undone.

Never tie the horse directly to the stable ring. Should the horse take fright and pull back, he may break the headcollar, pull the ring out, or slip up. If the weather is suitable, and the horse quiet, he can be groomed outside, but the yard gate must be closed. Tie him up to a suitable ring as before. Never tie him to a single post or tree, as he may move round, tangle himself up and have an accident. Never tie a horse to a gate: if he becomes unsettled, he could lift the gate off its hinges and panic.

If the weather is warm, remove the horse's rugs. In cold weather the rugs should be left on while you are attending to the horse's feet; a blanket should be placed over his loins while you are grooming his fore part, and over his shoulders and back while you are working on his hindquarters.

To pick out the feet, take the hoof pick and pick them out into a skip. Use the hoof pick in a downwards direction towards the ground. Start at the side of the frog, taking care not to damage the softer parts on either side of the frog and the cleft. Make sure the foot is really clean. Check for thrush and that the shoe is tight. With horses who are used to having their feet picked out, it saves time to pick them all out from the near side. The off fore is picked up from behind the near fore, and the off hind from behind the near hind.

It is usual to wash the feet on return from exercise. If the horse is in his stable, hold each foot over a bucket of water and scrub clean using an old dandy brush. Take care not to wet the foot above the bulbs of the heels.

To remove dry mud and sweat from the horse's body, use the rubber curry comb, or a handful of hay or straw, or the cactus cloth. If the horse is sensitive, use a dry water brush. Sticky patches of sweat can be sponged clean with warm water and dried with a towel.

To clean the coat, take the body brush in the left hand and the metal curry comb in the right hand. Start on the near side just behind the ears, push the mane over and thoroughly clean the crest, then work over the body. Stand well away from the horse, so that the full strength of the arm can be used to clean the coat. Brush in the direction of the hair, using both circular and straight movements of the brush to penetrate through to the skin. The hand holding the metal curry comb should rest on the horse's body, with the curry comb strap over the back of the hand. Clean the body brush with the curry comb as necessary. Clean the curry comb by knocking it on the ground near the door, so that the dust falls out. Sweep up the dust when the grooming is finished.

To brush the legs, put the curry comb on the ground away from the horse, and with the sharp side down. Use the body brush in whichever hand is most convenient and hold the horse's leg with the other. Crouch – do not kneel or sit – and keep your face away from the horse's knee.

When brushing the hind legs, if the horse is restless, hold his tail and hock with one hand and brush with the other. This prevents the horse from flexing his hock in preparation to kick, and also gives warning of any intention to do so. Stand near to the horse and keep a firm hold on his leg.

Grooming

To brush the mane, start at the poll, take a few hairs at a time and brush out thoroughly with the body brush. A short-pronged plastic curry comb can be used for this, but care must be taken not to break the hairs of the mane.

To brush the head, untie the horse, brush his face, then slip the headcollar down and buckle it around his neck. Steady the horse's head with one hand, and use the body brush gently in the other to clean the head. Pay particular attention to the lower jaw and gullet and around the ears. Take care not to knock or bruise the bony parts. It is important to be gentle, as horses can become head shy if they are roughly handled. When you have finished, put on the headcollar again and tie up the horse.

To bang or wisp, take the leather pad, wisp or folded stabled rubber and dampen it slightly. Stand back from the horse and vigorously bang it down on to the horse on the neck, shoulders, quarters and second thigh. Avoid the loins and bony parts. Use either hand, steadying the horse with the other.

To sponge, wash out the sponge and untie the horse, leaving the rope through the string. Gently but firmly clean the eyes, muzzle and nose, rinsing the sponge as required. Tie up the horse, rinse the sponge or take a second sponge, lift up the tail and clean around and under the dock. If the horse is restless, stand to one side, not immediately behind him.

To brush the tail, stand to the side of the horse, take the tail (approximately at the end of the dock) in one hand, and the body brush in the other. Allow a few hairs at a time to escape from the hand holding the tail, and gently brush these out, taking care not to break the hairs. With thin-tailed horses, it is best to use the fingers, not a brush. Finish by brushing out the top of the tail, dampening it down with a water brush and putting on a tail bandage. Dirty tails should be washed and then brushed out.
　　Never try to brush out a muddy tail. It must be washed.

To use the stable rubber, fold it into a pad, slightly dampen it and wipe the horse's body over to remove any remaining dust.

To lay the mane, tidy it with a damp water brush and stroke the hair into place.

Brush the rugs and then shake the blanket well away from the horse.

Oil the feet.

Untie the horse, leaving the headcollar on or removing it, according to the occasion and personal preference.

EXTRA GROOMING

Mane Washing
Collect warm water, horse shampoo, a large sponge, a towel and a sweat scraper. Put on a headcollar. To avoid staining his head, it may be necessary to fit a grey horse with a clean nylon headcollar or white rope halter. Do not tie the horse up. Wet the mane with the sponge. Starting with the forelock, thoroughly rub in the shampoo, keeping it well clear of the eyes. Continue down the mane. Rinse with warm water until all the soap has been removed. Remove surplus water from the neck with a sweat scraper, and rub the ears dry with a towel. Brush the mane out with a clean body brush or a plastic curry comb.

Tail Washing
Collect the washing equipment. Put on a headcollar and tie the horse up. If he is restless, ask an assistant to hold him, and to pick up a front leg if necessary. Proceed as for the mane, but soak the tail in a bucket of warm water. Take care, because when the water reaches the dock the horse may become disturbed. To dry the tail, stand to the side of the horse, hold the tail at the end of the dock and swish the bottom of the tail around in a circle. Brush out gently with a clean body brush.

Bathing the Horse
Bathing is a more extensive operation than washing or sponging down after work. It is carried out if there is a non-infectious skin problem, or as a quick measure to ensure a clean horse. Grey horses may have to be washed regularly, as they are difficult to get or keep clean. However, washing should never be a substitute for good grooming.

It is important for the horse to be thoroughly and quickly dried after bathing, so never wash him on a cold day. Lungeing him with a cavesson and boots on, or walking him out with a clean exercise blanket under the saddle are the best methods of keeping him warm and drying him off.

If possible, enlist the help of an assistant, and proceed as for mane washing. Wash the head first and then dry it with a towel. Tie up the horse and continue the process of washing, making sure that all the shampoo is thoroughly rinsed out. In warm weather, if the horse accepts it, a hose can be used. The legs should be given a final rinse with cold water. Use towels to dry off the horse, or a brisk rub with straw (though not on greys, as the straw may stain the coat). The legs must be bandaged either with Gamgee and stable bandages, or thatched with straw or hay to help them dry.

Bathing removes oil from the skin, and the horse's coat often looks a little dull afterwards. A good strapping will restore the bloom.

Washing White Legs
White legs should not be shampooed in cold weather. Warm water and soap remove the protective oils from the skin, and mud fever or cracked heels may result. However, barrier cream applied to dry, clean legs and heels can assist in preventing this. If there is urgent need, the legs may be individually washed down with cold water, and dried with stable bandages applied over hay or straw.

Spongeing Down
Spongeing down is used on a sweating horse after exercise, or at a competition.

Method

☐ If he is still blowing, lead the horse about until he is calm, and his breathing is normal. The girths should be eased, but the saddle left on. Alternatively, the saddle may be removed and the back slapped to restore circulation and then covered with a towel. In cold weather a sweat sheet and light rugs should be put on.

☐ Pick out the feet. Wash them if necessary.

☐ Remove the saddle and bridle and put on a headcollar. If an assistant is available, ask him to hold the horse.

☐ Wash the horse down, using a large sponge and plain water. In hot weather use cold water or, if the horse will accept it, the yard hose. In cold weather, use lukewarm water and sponge only the very sweaty areas. Never use really warm or hot water, as it is more likely to give the horse a chill.

☐ Remove surplus water with a sweat scraper.

☐ Put on a sweat sheet, rug, roller and breastplate, or alternatively straw beneath an inside-out rug, plus a roller and breastplate.

☐ Sponge round the base of the ears and face. Dry with a towel.

☐ Walk the horse about until he is dry. Ensure that the ears are dry and warm. In very cold weather put on stable bandages over hay or straw (thatching).

☐ After thirty minutes, check the rugs. If the horse is dry, groom him and put on his usual rugs.

Introducing the Horse to being Hosed
In warm weather hosing is a quick and efficient method of cleaning and cooling off a horse. However, at first most horses are nervous of being hosed down. When first introducing hosing to the horse it is helpful to have a second person to hold him. Start gently with little pressure, and

apply the resultant trickle around the front feet. Gradually work up the leg. At no time must the horse be frightened. As he begins to accept the sensation, gradually increase the pressure. When horses become used to the water they usually enjoy it, but some never accept it, and where they are concerned it is best to abandon the process.

Washing the Sheath
Some geldings require regular washing of the sheath. The signs that this is needed are a strong smell and nodules of greasy dirt collecting in and around the sheath. An assistant may be required to hold the horse and possibly to hold up a front leg. The equipment needed is a bucket of warm water, mild soap, a sponge and rubber gloves. Soak the sheath and thoroughly clean out as much as the horse will allow. Then dry it with a towel.

WASHING THE GROOMING KIT

All items in the grooming kit should be washed with detergent weekly. Dip the bristles, but do not wet the backs more than necessary. Rinse thoroughly. Dry the brushes by standing them on their sides in a dry atmosphere, but not near direct heat. Leather-backed brushes should be oiled. Stable rubbers should be washed twice a week, or as necessary. As a safeguard against infection, it is best that each horse has his own grooming kit.

MAKING A WISP

Shake out a length of meadow hay on the ground and dampen it. With the help of an assistant, twist the hay into a rope, make two loops at one end and twist the remaining rope in and out of the loops. Tuck the ends away firmly, then thump the wisp hard. A well-made wisp is firm, secure and small enough to hold in the hand. It should last several weeks.

BUYING A GROOMING KIT

The more expensive brushes last longer and are easier and more efficient to use. The bristles tend to fall out of cheaper, machine-made brushes.

Body Brushes
These should be of soft natural bristle. Leather backs are preferable to wood, but both are suitable.

Dandy Brushes
These are wooden backed, and the bristles are of a much tougher texture than those of a body brush. Some dandy brushes are made of coloured nylon tufts. Some horses are allergic to nylon, and these brushes clog more easily. Natural bristle is preferable.

Water Brushes
These should be wooden backed, with long, soft, natural bristle.

Grooming equipment can be bought in various sizes. For efficient use, it should fit the hand of the user.

GROOMING THE GRASS-KEPT HORSE OR PONY

In Winter

Method

- ☐ Tie the horse up as before.

- ☐ Wash and pick out the feet. Check for any nails or stones which might have been picked up, and for cracked heels.

- ☐ When the horse is dry, remove the mud from his coat with the dandy brush or plastic curry comb. The latter is more efficient. Pay particular attention to the saddle and girth areas. Clean the head carefully, using the body brush or your hand. Sweat marks should have been washed off after work, before the horse was turned out. If small patches have been left in the saddle area, clean them off with warm soapy water and then rinse with cold water. Wet mud on the legs, knees and hocks may be washed off with cold water and the legs left to dry. Do not use warm water and soap, as this will open the pores of the skin, making the legs more vulnerable to cracked heels and mud fever. It is preferable to leave wet mud until it is dry and then brush it off. Clean the dandy brush by brushing it against the sharp surface of a wall or door, well away from the horse. The plastic curry comb may be cleaned by knocking it against a similar surface. Sponge the eyes, nose, muzzle and dock area.

☐ Clean the mane with the dandy brush or plastic curry comb.

☐ If the tail is muddy, wash it then brush it out. If it is dry and clean, brush it out with the body brush, not the plastic curry comb. The curry comb should be used only on the bottom 16cm (6in) of the tail. The hairs on a horse's tail, which are easily broken off by rough brushing, take up to two years to grow. Thin-tailed horses and ponies should always have their tails brushed out with a body brush, or simply with the fingers.

☐ The feet, when dry, can be oiled if required.

In Summer
When grooming for a special occasion, for instance a show or rally, the procedure is similar to that for grooming a stabled horse, but with less emphasis on cleaning down to the skin.

GROOMING MACHINES

There are several different types of grooming machines on the market, such as:

The vacuum type, with a suction head, which can be used for removing dirt/mud or loose coat in the spring. It is of particular value on horses who have been blanket or trace clipped.

The revolving brush type, which can be recommended for the large yard, when there is insufficient time for daily strapping.

The more modern machines are light and come with a waist belt which fastens round the waist of the operator. This makes them easier to handle than older machines. They have a dust bag attached, which collects all the loose hair and dust.

The stable manager should ensure that staff in the yard do not use the machines as an excuse for inadequate daily care.

A muddy, grass-kept horse or pony required for a special occasion can be effectively cleaned up by the suction-type fixture. This removes mud and dirt, but leaves much of the grease in the coat. Make sure that the coat is quite dry before using the machine.

Because of labour costs, in many racing yards daily strapping has been discontinued. The horses are brushed over and tidied each day. After fast work they are sponged down. They are usually done over with a grooming machine every four to seven days. It has been found that they remain quite healthy and are considerably better tempered in the stable as a result of not being subjected to intense grooming and strapping.

Safety Rules
The operator should wear an overall, headscarf or cap, and rubber boots and the machine should be plugged into a circuit breaker. Great care must be taken not to catch the mane or tail in the machine. The tail should be roughly plaited, and then bandaged.

Horses who are difficult to clip often accept a grooming machine and then become easier to manage during

Grooming

clipping. Grooming machines are excellent for cleaning the coat, and the vibratory action of the brush has a stimulating effect on the skin, which is generally much enjoyed by the horse. Care must be taken to use only soft brushes on a thin-coated horse.

The machine should not be used more frequently than once every three days, and the day after hunting or any extra exertion. If it is used too often, the skin may become tender and sore.

CHAPTER 4
Bedding

Bedding is material which is put on the floor of a loosebox or stall to:

Encourage the horse to lie down and rest.

Enable him to do so in comfort, without risk of injury.

Keep him warm and minimise draughts.

Encourage him to stale.

Reduce jar to his legs from standing and moving around on a hard surface.

Prevent him slipping up when moving about the stable.

Bedding is also used in a trailer or horsebox when a horse is travelling to cover the floor and to give a softer and less slippery surface.

TYPES OF BEDDING

Straw
Straw is still the most widely used bedding.

Wheat straw. Modern farming methods have resulted in wheat being grown with a much shorter stalk. When baled it is often heavily compacted and brittle, affecting its durability and reducing its value as bedding. Good wheat straw makes excellent bedding but it is not easily available.

Barley straw is usually longer, of better quality and a brighter colour than wheat straw. Modern combine harvesting removes the awns which used to irritate the horse's skin.

Oat straw is palatable and more expensive. It quickly becomes saturated, which makes it the least suitable straw for bedding.

If it is of good quality, straw of any type is likely to be eaten by the horse. In a similar way to hay, the straw and dust will be a host to fungal spores. When inhaled by the horse these can cause, or re-activate, allergic coughing. The eating of straw can cause common horses to become gross and can affect the fitness of horses in fast work. Disinfectant sprayed on the bed helps to discourage the eating of straw.

Advantages

The bed has a clean, bright appearance.

Straw manure can be disposed of more easily than other types.

In a good harvest year it can be cheap.

Disadvantages

It can be eaten by the horse and is likely to cause allergic coughing.

The manure is heavy.

In a bad harvest year it can be very expensive.

Straw Deep Litter

Advantages

It is economical. Once the bed has been put down (plenty of

straw must be used) the daily requirement will be less than for a conventional straw bed.

It is warm.

It provides a solid bed. The horse cannot get through to the floor when rolling, and there is less risk of injury.

It is labour saving on a daily basis.

It is suitable for use where there is an uneven floor or poor drainage.

When mucking out there is less disturbance of the bed, so that fewer fungal spores and less dust are released into the atmosphere.

Disadvantages

It can be unsightly and unhygienic if it is badly managed.

It is not suitable for restless or very dirty horses as it will be impossible to keep them clean.

Extra care must be taken to ensure that the horses' feet remain healthy.

If the bed starts to smell, remove it, disinfect the floor and put down a new bed. This is usually a sign of bad management.

The eventual cleaning out is very heavy work and requires extra help. A tractor and trailer can be useful. It should be done when the height of the bed becomes inconvenient, which can take from one to three months.

Shavings and Sawdust
These may be collected locally, or compressed baled shavings may now be bought from corn merchants or by direct delivery from manufacturers. Shavings are generally preferable to sawdust as they are less dusty.

Advantages

They provide a spore-free bed.

Bedding

They will not be eaten by the horse, therefore his fitness and weight will not be affected.

The bed is lighter to work with than straw.

There will be less smell on clothes.

Grey horses will be easier to keep clean.

In some areas shavings and sawdust can be collected free.

Baled shavings are packed in polythene bags for easy storage and are comparatively dust free.

They may be used with advantage on an uneven floor where there is no drainage.

Disadvantages

Some samples may be dusty. They may require damping down when the bed is first laid.

They cannot be used for horses with open wounds.

Manure may be difficult to dispose of, although it can be burnt.

Shavings, if sharp, may irritate the heels of some horses.

Rugs cannot be put down in a corner of the box as in a straw bed.

Care must be taken when putting down any articles, including grooming equipment.

If the bed round the walls is left undisturbed and allowed to compact and to heat, there is a risk of the wooden walls rotting. To avoid this, the bottom 60cm (2ft) of the wall should be treated with black bitumen paint.

Shredded Paper

Shredded newspaper or waste paper from offices can be bought by the bale. It is also possible to buy a shredder and to cut paper on the yard.

Advantages

It provides a totally dust- and spore-free bed, so it is excellent for horses who are allergic to straw and dust.

Being packed in polythene bags, it is easy to store.

It is easily disposed of because it can be burnt when dry, or put on to gardens when broken down. It breaks down more quickly than other types of bedding.

Disadvantages

It is unattractive to look at.

It needs very careful management.

Horses with white legs may be allergic to printer's ink.

Merchants may be unwilling to collect the manure.

It can be more expensive than other types of bedding.

Problems may arise in keeping the yard and muck heap tidy.

Peat Moss
This is seldom used.

Advantages

It can be used on gardens when rotted down.

It is suitable for horses with fungal spore allergies, or for confirmed bed-eaters.

Disadvantages

It is a difficult bed to manage and is dusty when put down.

The dark colour means that wet parts of the bed are not easily visible.

Horses become easily stained

It cannot be burned.

PUTTING DOWN THE BED – GENERAL PRINCIPLES

Whatever the type of bedding used, the bed should be between 15cm (6in) and 30cm (12in) deep. A good bed will make a horse feel better and work better. Banks round the sides to a height of 30cm (12in) increase warmth, lessen draughts and give some protection should a horse become cast. For added warmth the bed should if possible be taken up to the door.

TAKING THE BED UP

In many stables the bed (if it is not deep litter) is taken up during the day, the floor allowed to dry and a thin layer of straw spread on the floor.

Advantages

If there is a drying wind the floor will dry and so, too, will some of the bedding.

Disadvantages

There is a danger of a horse slipping on the floor.

There is a danger of a horse lying down on an insufficient bed and injuring himself.

On a damp day the floor will not dry.

Bedding the horse down in the morning saves time and labour in the evening, when time is always short. A good bed in the day adds greatly to the comfort and well-being of a horse.

The only way to economise on bedding without detriment to the horse is to check on the amount of usable bedding which is put on the muck heap in the morning. Any usable bedding should be kept; clean bedding should be mixed with it and spread over the top. It is all too easy to throw away clean bedding which has dung on top of it instead of shaking it clear. This is not to say that horses should have dirty or wet beds. The principle is to provide good beds but not to waste bedding.

MANAGEMENT OF BEDDING

Equipment

Long-handled two-pronged fork, usually known as a pitchfork or hay fork. The handle should be of a length appropriate for the height and build of the groom. These forks are not suitable for picking up manure and wet straw. They should be used for shaking up the straw bales and for shaking up the bed when it is being relaid. In careless hands they can be dangerous if used when the horse is in the box. It is easy to misjudge the weight or depth of a forkful of straw and to nick the horse on the leg. A wise precaution is to have the ends of the prongs blunted.

Four-pronged fork, short or long handle. A tall groom may find the long-handled type more comfortable as it will necessitate less bending, but the short-handled fork is easier to manage and to control. The ends should not be sharp. The fork is used for mucking out straw bedding and for spreading other types.

Twelve-pronged or close-pronged lightweight fork usually known as a stone fork. The prongs are close together. This is used for collecting dung particles from a shavings, sawdust or similar bed.

Shovel, of a suitable weight for the groom. Very light shovels rapidly rust from contact with urine.

Brooms. Small nylon brooms are easy to handle and are hard wearing. The wider, heavier brooms are more suitable for male grooms. Small, soft brooms with long handles are useful for sweeping walls and for removing cobwebs.

Bedding

Yard brooms, 60 to 90cm (2 to 3ft) wide, are excellent for yard sweeping but soon wear if used in the stable. Brooms are made of birch or nylon tufts. Both materials give good wear. The handles must be of a suitable length and size for the user.

Skip. This is used for collecting the droppings from the bed; the droppings are either scooped or forked into it. Plastic washing skips are cheap, suitable and easy to keep clean.

Wire rake. This is used for raking shavings beds. The type used for raking moss out of a lawn ('Springbok') is suitable.

Rubber gloves may be used to skip out a box by hand, particularly when the bed is of shavings or sawdust.

Wheelbarrows. Lightweight wheelbarrows are not suitable, as they quickly rust through and do not stand up to the work required of them. Two-wheeled barrows are expensive but they are easy to load, very stable and easy to push. Single-wheeled barrows are suitable providing they are made of a heavy metal, but they are hard to push and easily turn over. Wooden wheelbarrows are heavy and not recommended.

Before using, it is worthwhile giving the inside of all wheelbarrows a second coat of paint. This gives them some added protection – an undercoat of rust-resistant paint gives even better protection.

Split polypyrene muck sacks with rope handles may be used instead of wheelbarrows for conveying stable manure to the muck heap. They are easier to fill than wheelbarrows, but heavy to carry. When swinging them on to the back it is easy to strain a muscle. They are easily washed clean.

Split jute sacks were formerly used but these are now difficult to obtain. They tend to become saturated and unpleasant to handle.

All stable tools should be washed regularly – at least once

a week. This improves their appearance, makes brooms more efficient to use, and makes shovels last longer. Wheelbarrows profit from being washed out daily and then stood up so that the water drains out. If left in contact with urine and manure, metal will quickly rust.

When not in use, all stable tools should be hung up in a dry shed. This lengthens their useful life and means that in frosty weather grooms will not have to contend with ice on the handles. Stable tools, particularly forks and rakes with long handles, can be a hazard if left about for either staff or horses to trip over or stand on. Tidiness and care in the use of stable tools is a must.

PREPARATION OF THE BOX BEFORE PUTTING DOWN A NEW BED

Equipment

☐ Long-handled two-pronged fork.

☐ Four-pronged fork.

☐ Shovel.

☐ Wheelbarrow.

☐ Hard broom for sweeping up and scrubbing walls.
☐ Soft broom for sweeping walls and ceiling.

☐ Large sponge for washing windows.

☐ Leather for polishing windows, or window-cleaning equipment.

☐ Water bucket.

☐ Can of disinfectant.

☐ Well-built step-ladder for reaching ceilings and windows.

Method

☐ Take the horse out of the box.

Bedding

☐ Remove old bedding and water.

☐ Dust walls, ceilings and windows.

☐ Clean out and wash fixed mangers. Cover them with polythene bags to keep them clean.

☐ Wash and clean windows.

☐ Wash and scrub floor. Leave to dry.

☐ Put down bed.

☐ Check stable for dust, and re-do if necessary.

☐ Clean and re-fill water buckets or water bowl.

☐ Check fixed manger. Remove polythene cover and clean again if necessary.

PUTTING DOWN THE BED

Straw

Equipment

☐ Long-handled fork.

☐ Broom.

☐ Sufficient bales of straw, the number depending on the size of the box, the weight of the bales and the quality of the straw. The bed should be from 23 to 30cm (9 to 12in) thick, with straw banks round the sides 30 to 45cm (12 to 18in) high.

Method

☐ Prepare the box as described above.

☐ Shake up the straw – this is sometimes easier to do by hand.

☐ With the fork, spread the straw evenly over the floor, flattening the lower level to make it solid.

☐ Shake the top straw evenly over the bed.

☐ Bank the remaining straw round the walls. Make the banks by walking backwards round the box, flattening the straw up against the wall with the back of the fork.

☐ For special occasions the straw by the door may be plaited or turned in during the day. This is done by placing a long-handled fork or broom on top of the straw and then turning it under or plaiting it. At night it should be banked up against the door to prevent draughts.

Straw Deep Litter

Equipment
As already detailed.

Method
As for a conventional straw bed.

In addition
The bed should be between 30 and 45cm (12 and 18in) thick, and the lower levels should be beaten down with a fork to compact the straw. Four to six bales will be required. Banks should be 30cm (12in) above the surface of the bed.

Shavings

Equipment

☐ As already detailed, plus rake. A two-pronged fork is not required.

☐ A suitable quantity of bags of shavings.

Method

☐ Prepare the box as described above.

☐ Seal off all covered drains to prevent blockage by the shavings. Use a removable fitted top or a small plastic bag filled with sawdust and fitted into the drain.

Bedding

☐ Shake out sufficient bags of shavings to make a bed between 15 and 23cm (6 and 9in) deep.

☐ Spread the shavings with the four-pronged fork.

☐ Damp down, if dusty, with a watering can or by splashing water out of a bucket by hand.

☐ Put extra shavings around the walls to make a good solid bank.

NB Shavings obtained from local sawmills should always be checked for rubbish, pieces of wood, plastic cups, etc. Baled shavings from merchants are usually free of rubbish.

Sawdust

Equipment

☐ As already detailed, plus a wire rake. A two-pronged fork is not required.

☐ A suitable quantity of bags of sawdust.

Method

☐ Prepare the box as described above.

☐ Block the drains as above.

☐ Shake out the sawdust and spread it with the shovel to a depth of 15 to 23cm (6 to 9in).

☐ Rake the sawdust level.

☐ Spread more sawdust round the sides and bank it up the walls, using the shovel.

☐ Check the material for rubbish.

Shavings or Sawdust Deep Litter

Equipment

☐ As already detailed. A two-pronged fork is not required.

Method
As for a conventional shavings or sawdust bed.

Shredded Paper

Paper is a difficult bedding to manage because it blows about so easily. Wheelbarrows need to be covered. If necessary, a bucket of water may be poured over the barrow's contents before they are emptied. New bedding on the muck heap should be well covered with old manure to prevent it blowing about.

Equipment

☐ As already detailed. A two-pronged fork is not required.

☐ Three to four bales of compressed paper.

Method

☐ Prepare the box as described above.

☐ Seal off the drains, as above.

☐ Shake out the paper *thoroughly*, either using the four-pronged fork or by hand.

☐ Spread the bed evenly with the fork to a depth of 23cm (9in).

☐ Bank the bed up the walls.

☐ Flatten the lower layers to make a more solid bed.

Peat Moss

Equipment

☐ As already detailed. A two-pronged fork is not required.

☐ Three to four bales of peat moss.

Method

☐ Prepare the box as described above.

Bedding

- [ ] Seal off the drains, as above.
- [ ] Shake out the peat moss and, using the four-pronged fork and the shovel, spread it to a depth of 15 to 23cm (6 to 9in).
- [ ] Rake it level and bank it up the walls, again using the fork and shovel.

DAILY PROGRAMME

Morning

- [ ] Muck out.
- [ ] Set fair the bed.
- [ ] Sweep up the stable area and yard.

Midday

- [ ] Skip the box out (the box should be skipped out throughout the day).

NB   The horse should be tied up whilst the box is skipped out.

Evening

- [ ] Skip the box out.
- [ ] Add fresh bedding if required.
- [ ] Set the box fair.
- [ ] Sweep the yard and leave everything tidy for the night.

If labour is available, the yard can also be swept at midday.

MUCKING OUT

Method

- [ ] Collect equipment.

☐ Put a headcollar on the horse. If the headcollar is left on during the day (with the rope removed) time will be saved when attending to the horse, when skipping out the box and at evening stables.

Either:

Tie the horse up in his box.   The disadvantages are that he is then exposed to dust and fungal spores if straw bedding is used, and to dust if shavings, sawdust or peat moss are used. It is quicker to muck out a box if the horse is not in it.

Or:

Tie the horse up outside the box.   This should only be done, when outside looseboxes are used, if the horse is used to it and if the weather is dry. It is not advisable on a windy or very cold day. The yard gate should be closed. With inside boxes it is convenient to have the horse out of the box. However, when he is tied in the passageway he causes an obstruction and may be a hazard if other, neighbouring horses are also tied up outside their boxes. It is likely that he will still be within inhaling distance of fungal spores and dust caused by the shaking up of a straw bale.

Or:

Tie the horse up in a spare loosebox.   This is the preferable arrangement, though it should not be considered if there is any virus infection or other problem in the yard.

All stabling should be kept as dust free as possible.

Walls should be dusted down daily.

Whatever bedding is used, mucking out is a time-consuming task. Any new ideas or systems which can shorten the process of both mucking out and sweeping the yard, without loss of efficiency, must be of benefit to both staff and management.

Bedding

Labour-Saving Ideas

Deep litter.

The use of a tractor and trailer.

The putting of manure direct into transportable skips which are collected, when full, by a contractor.

An automatic sweeper.

Barn-type stabling.

Split sacks or polypyrene muck sacks with rope handles, which are easier to fill than barrows, though they can be heavy to move.

Straw Bedding

During the process of mucking out and shaking up a straw bed, there is a very considerable increase in the amount of fungal spores and dust in the atmosphere. This is not good for any horse but has a disastrous effect on those animals who suffer from allergic coughing and/or COPD. If possible, whenever straw is to be shaken up, the horse should be out of the box. With interior barn stabling, consideration should be given to horses in adjacent boxes.

Daily Care

Skip out the bed regularly during the day – the horse should be tied up – using the skip.

Evening Stables (between 4.00pm and 5.30pm)

Tie the horse up.

Skip out the bed.

Shake up and re-arrange the bed, adding fresh bedding if required.

Empty and refill water buckets.

Untie the horse and remove headcollar.

Empty the skip either into a wheelbarrow or straight on to the muck heap.

NB   It is timesaving and convenient to hang a skip on the outside wall of a stable so that it is always available.

Except with deep litter beds, the floor should be washed regularly with disinfectant, preferably when the horse can be out of the stable for an hour.

THE MUCK HEAP

Siting and construction are covered in Book 6, *The Stable Yard*.

Building the Muck Heap
The muck heap requires daily care. If the manure is thrown up, it must be built in steps with a flat top. This construction allows the muck heap to absorb rain, which assists in the rotting-down process. The sides must be kept vertical and well-raked down and the surrounding area swept up and kept clean. If it can be arranged for the approach path to be higher than the muck heap, wheelbarrows may be emptied by tipping them, which saves time and effort. It is also possible to have a pit dug for the same purpose, though this type of muck heap may be difficult to empty by fork-lift lorries. Whatever the type of muck heap, the actual building and raking must still be done each day. An untidy muck heap is a disgrace to a stable yard and reflects badly on both management and staff.

Disposal of Manure
It is essential to try to make satisfactory arrangements for the disposal of manure. Regular collections may be undertaken by contract with firms supplying market gardens and mushroom growers. Local farmers may be willing to spread stable manure on their fields, but ensure that they do collect it regularly, not just once a year. Large yards, which can

guarantee a regular supply, should have no problem, but it can be difficult for the small yard, which only stables horses in winter. The financial aspect is of little importance compared with regular cleaning. In the past, some firms would only accept wheat-straw manure. However, as straw-only manure has become less readily available, it has become easier to get rid of the mixed muck heap, including paper bedding.

It is not recommended that horse manure be spread on fields belonging to the yard, unless these are to be ploughed. There is an increased danger of worm infestation and such fields are likely to become 'horse sick', an ever-present problem in equestrian establishments.

Disposal of Shavings and Sawdust Manure
Within reason, shavings and sawdust manure may be added to the floor of an indoor school, where it quickly becomes absorbed in the base. Alternatively, it may be heaped up and burnt. Choose an area well away from roads and buildings, as the fire will be continuous. Some manure firms will collect a mixed straw and shavings load. It may also be built up, away from the yard, and allowed to rot down before being sold as garden compost. The rotting-down process may be hastened by the use of chemicals, otherwise it may take up to two years.

Disposal of Paper Bedding Manure
Paper bedding manure breaks down quickly and may be spread within a few weeks or used as mushroom compost. It should not be put on to a grass surface to form a riding track because in wet weather the track will become slippery and dangerous.

CHAPTER 5

Clipping, Trimming, Pulling and Plaiting

CLIPPING

Clipping is the removal of the horse's coat by machine. A horse changes his coat twice a year. From mid-September to mid-October he grows a thick winter coat, and between February and April he loses his winter coat and grows a light summer one. The old coat may become rough and dull during the period of change, particularly in the autumn. The exact timing varies between different types of horses and ponies, and is also affected by weather and temperature.

The growth of coat also varies for a stabled horse; the temperature of the stable and the number of rugs worn are the major influences. A well-bred horse, stabled and rugged throughout the year, grows a very light winter coat, and if he is not in hard, fast work, he may not require clipping.

Grass-kept horses and ponies are left unclipped to give them protection from the weather. If they are in steady work, they benefit from a semi-trace clip, or the removal of the coat on the shoulder and underneath the neck, in October and early November. This makes work easier and avoids any heavy sweating, which can occur if there is a warm spell of weather in October. Ponies protected by a New Zealand rug can be regularly trace clipped up until January.

The reasons for clipping a stabled horse are:

To prevent distress when he is in hard, fast work. This is applicable in winter when the coat is thick, and sometimes even in spring and summer if the horse is expected to work at maximum effort, for example in three-day eventing or long-distance riding.

To help keep him in good condition. Sweating leads to weight loss.

To make drying off after work quicker.

To save time and labour over cleaning.

To prevent and/or to control skin disease.

The first clip takes place in late September/early October. The weather is often very warm, and a working horse benefits from the removal of his coat. Overweight horses brought in after a summer at grass may have their clipping delayed to encourage sweating and a consequent loss of flesh. Well-bred horses may require clipping only every four weeks; heavy-coated animals may need clipping every two or three weeks, if they are to look tidy and smart. A horse who is to be shown should not be clipped after the end of January, as late clips spoil the summer coat.

Show Horses
The owner must decide whether or not to clip show horses. It depends on the individual horse, his type of coat and whether his finer points need to be shown or concealed. If the decision is to clip, in all cases the horse is given a full clip. Coarse blades may be used to give a more natural look.

Show Ponies
Ponies who are slow to establish their summer coat, or who

have a rough coat, need to be clipped, particularly if they are being shown early in the season.

Three-Day Event and Long-Distance Riding Horses
Horses used in these two sports may be clipped immediately before the competition.

TYPES OF CLIP AND THEIR USE

Full Clip
The entire coat is removed, including the legs and saddle patch. A triangle is left at the top of the tail. The clip may be used on coarse-coated hunters. It makes them easier to clean and quicker to dry off, particularly the legs. It is often used only for the first and second clips. Thereafter the horse does not grow such a heavy coat, and a normal hunter clip can be used.

If a coarser blade is used for the saddle patch and legs, some protective hair will be left. Many people consider that even with well-bred horses, if the long hair is left on the legs, it makes them slower to dry, more difficult to keep clean and therefore more liable to mud fever.

Full Clip Except for Saddle Patch
The saddle patch is left on to ease saddle pressure. Thin-skinned Thoroughbred horses are often best left with the saddle patch on.

Hunter Clip
The legs (to just below the elbow and stifle joint) and the saddle patch are left unclipped. Hair on the legs gives protection from the cold, and from thorns, mud fever and cracked heels. The saddle patch gives some protection from saddle friction.

Chaser Clip
Hair is removed from the head and lower two-thirds of the

Hunter clip.

Chaser clip.

Blanket clip.

Trace clip.

neck and body. The coat is left on from behind the ear and over the top part of the body to the tail.

Alternative to the Chaser Clip
Hair is removed below a line starting at the stifle joint, along to the bottom of the saddle flap, up the neck to the base of the ears and down the side of the face.

Blanket Clip
Hair is removed from the head, neck, shoulder and belly and a narrow strip on either side of the dock, thus giving the shape of an exercise sheet.

The above three clips are used for:

Horses brought into work during the winter who require walking exercise in cold weather.

Young horses in their first season's hunting.

Horses who are cold backed or who easily catch chills.

Show jumpers kept in work during the winter.

Trace Clip
Hair is removed in a strip from the shoulder, belly and thighs, and often from the under part of the neck.

This clip is used for:

Horses who resent having their heads clipped. For them, the line of the clip is taken well up the shoulder, belly and thigh.

Horses in light work.

Horses and ponies turned out in New Zealand rugs.

PREPARATION FOR CLIPPING

A warm, still day is best. Start as early in the day as possible.

The Stable
Good lighting is essential. A utility box with a non-slip

rubber floor is ideal. If this is not available, a spare box may be used, preferably with a shavings bed, as this makes it easier to pick up the clipped hair. Horses should not be clipped on a bare floor, because of the risk of slipping and the danger from electricity if the floor becomes wet. If a horse has to be clipped in his own box, ensure that the bed is dry and well flattened. Clean straw should not be added until the clipped hair has been collected. The hair can be put into a paper sack and then burned.

*A **haynet*** should be tied up in the box to keep the horse occupied.

*A **skip*** should be placed outside the loosebox.

*A **strong box or straw bale*** should be available for standing on when clipping the horse's head.

The horse should be clean and dry. A dirty coat clogs the blades, causes overheating and strains the machine. The blades cannot cut a damp coat. If a horse becomes upset and breaks out in a sweat, it is best to stop clipping until he has settled and dried off.

*A **grooming machine*** can be a great boon, both to ensure a clean horse and to get the animal used to the noise and vibration of a machine. If a horse is known to be difficult, ensure that experienced help is available, and that sufficient time has been allowed to avoid any hurrying.

After clipping, the horse can be brushed over with a dampened body brush, which will help to remove any surface scurf. An extra blanket will be needed for warmth.

The person handling the clippers should wear rubber boots or rubber-soled shoes as a safeguard against an electric shock. Overalls and a headscarf or cap protect clothes and hair from clipped hair.

With a difficult horse, the holder and clipper are at risk. They may have their feet trodden or stamped on, or receive a glancing blow from the horse's head. They should wear strong boots and hard hats. The assistant should also wear gloves which will make the rope easier to hold. They must never place themselves in front of the horse in case he should strike out. When required, the assistant should hold up the horse's front foot, standing facing the shoulder and holding the front of the foot in the palm of the hand with the fingers. The rope can then be held in the other hand.

THE ELECTRIC CLIPPING MACHINE

There are two popular types of mains electric clipping machines. There are also smaller battery-driven machines suitable for trimming, clipping heads and for use on thin-skinned, nervous or difficult horses.

The Hand Machine
The engine and clipping head are contained in one machine, with a cable to a mains power plug. This is small enough to hold in the hand. It is an efficient type of machine, excellent for the small yard or private owner clipping clean, stabled horses.

The Hanging or Heavy-Duty Type
These are suitable for the large commercial yard where many horses of all types have to be clipped. The machine itself is separate from the clipping head, and is connected by a flexible driving shaft. The machine is heavy and must be suspended from a beam or wall bracket. The actual clipping head is light, but the flexible shaft makes it less easy to manoeuvre, and there is more vibration than with a hand machine. It does give a very clean cut. If possible, such a machine should be kept in a loosebox or utility box reserved for clipping. Grooming machines may also be kept in this box. It will be easier to move the machine about if it is suspended on overhead runners.

Clipping with a heavy-duty machine will be easier if the driving shaft is kept as extended as possible. It requires regular oiling and greasing.

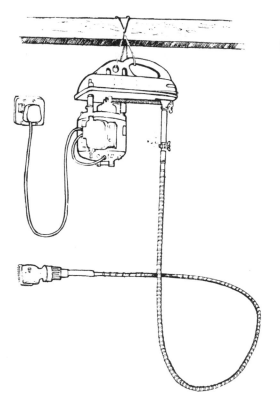

Heavy-duty clippers.

Battery Machine
This is attached to the user's back and is independent of any mains cable. It is battery powered and therefore safer. The clipping head is light and easily handled. As with all clipping machines, it is essential not to overheat the machine by clipping for too long at a time. The blades must be kept clean and oiled.

Electrical Connections
Electric machines should always be plugged into a power point. Those which are not self-earthed require a three-wire cable correctly connected to a three-pin plug to ensure safe earthing and should be connected to a circuit breaker. The correct cable and working instructions are supplied by the

manufacturers. The instruction booklet should be kept with the machine, and the makers' instructions followed.

Self-earthed machines should not be used from a light socket as this is not safe. Should the cable be pulled, either the light socket or the wiring will give way.

The Blades

The clipping blades must be sharp. Blunt blades are uncomfortable for the horse, give an uneven clip and strain and overheat the machine. A spare pair of new or resharpened blades should be available before clipping begins. New blades used on clean horses with fine coats may be expected to complete up to six clips, but on a heavy, dirty coat they soon become blunt and require resharpening. Resharpening is successful if carried out by an expert. Blades can easily be spoilt if they are incorrectly sharpened.

Blades are packed as a pair. The bottom plate is flat, and is fitted first. The top plate is placed on top of it. They are secured together by a flat-topped bolt, a tension spring and a thumb screw adjustment. Correct tension is essential. If it is too loose, the machine races and does not cut. If it is too tight, the machine is strained and overheats.

When the machine is switched on, light machine oil should be run through the blades and into the oil holes on top of the machine. The machine should be wiped clean before clipping starts. While clipping, the blades must be regularly cleaned. Brush them with a soft brush and then run the machine through a container of paraffin or methylated spirit, which removes dirt and hair. Because paraffin can blister the horse's skin, and oil may mark it, suitable precautions must be taken.

Should the machine heat up, stop clipping, clean it and allow it to cool. It may be necessary to fit fresh blades.

When the clipping is finished, remove and clean the blades, then clean and oil the machine, following the maker's instructions. The thumb screw and tension spring and bolt should be put back on the machine. Wrap the blades in oiled cloth, and store carefully. It is all too easy to drop the blades and chip them. A light knock is sufficient to put them off true, and thus give a strained and uneven clip. After clipping, always check the cable for wear. If the outer casing is worn, it may be made temporarily safe with insulating tape, but a new cable should be fitted as soon as possible.

Electric clippers, and in particular hand machines, are often ill used and prone to strain. They can easily seize up in the middle of a clip. It is sensible to have a replacement machine available in case this occurs.

HOW TO CLIP

If a mains hand clipper is being used first assemble the machine. Carry out a safety check, including an inspection for any signs of wear of the cable and the plug. Take the machine to the clipping box. Ensure that there is machine oil, a container of paraffin or methylated spirits, a soft brush, spare blades and chalk for marking lines. All this equipment should be placed safely out of the way on a shelf outside the box.

Plug in the machine, and check that it is working correctly. Switch it off, and put it in a safe place. Ensure that the cable can be suspended over a hook, so that when you are clipping it comes directly to the hand, and does not lie on the floor where the horse can tread on it. Check, too, that the horse cannot reach it with his teeth.

Bring the horse into the box and tie him up. If it is warm enough, remove his rugs, placing them well out of the way. If it is cold and draughty, place a blanket over his loins and back. Pick up the machine and switch it on. Allow the horse to become used to the noise before starting to clip.

When clipping start at the shoulder.

Switch off the machine and untie the horse, leaving the rope through the safety loop. Hold the end of the rope in the left hand, switch on the machine and then place the left hand on the horse's neck. Start on the near side, and clip the shoulder, running the machine against the direction of the hair. The line taken depends on which clip is required. Keep the machine flat. Do not push it; guide it and allow the machine to do the work. At all times clip against the growth of hair. When the shoulder, neck and chest on the near side have been finished, the horse may be tied up. The front part of the belly is then done, the blanket moved forward and the quarters, back and belly completed. The off side is then clipped. The machine may be held in either hand and changed if required.

Ticklish or difficult parts, such as the head, underneath of the belly, loins and in between the hind legs can be left to last, when an assistant may be required. When clipping around the elbow and chest, a front leg should be held up to help stretch the skin and avoid nicking it. Similarly, hold the skin taut when doing the stifle joint and flank area.

When clipping a front leg of a fidgety horse, the other front leg may be held up by an assistant to prevent the horse snatching up his leg and possibly breaking the clipping blades.

It is important to check that the machine is not over-heating. This is bad for the machine, and makes the horse fidgety and resentful.

For a Saddle Patch
Outline with chalk around the horse's own saddle. Make sure the outline is even and regular. Clip into the hair and lift the blades to achieve a tidy line.

For a Blanket or Trace Clip
Ensure an accurate and matching clip on both sides by measuring over the withers and back, and putting chalk lines on the horse's coat. The top of the front and hind legs should be clipped to the same height and angle. The clip should extend over the elbow to assist cleaning.

To Clip Up the Neck
Run the blade as close as possible to the mane hair. It is preferable to leave a narrow edge of coat, rather than cut into the mane.

Clipping of Mane
A small portion of mane may be removed where the bridle headpiece lies over the poll. This should not exceed 2.5cm (1in). A small section may also be removed at the top of the withers. In each case, if too much hair is clipped, it is unsightly. On a fine-maned animal, trimming is often better done with scissors, as it is very easy to remove too much with clippers.

DIFFICULT HORSES

Horses who resent having their heads or other ticklish parts clipped often accept a twitch on the nose, and will stand without struggling and allow the clip to be finished quickly and efficiently. In some cases, it is sufficient if the assistant holds the nose or ear with his hand. The twitch should never be put on a horse's ear. For use of the twitch see Chapter 1, *Restraint.*

Some highly-strung horses will not accept a twitch, and become violent if one is used. In such cases it can be dangerous to persevere and attempts to apply a twitch should be abandoned. If it is only a question of tidying up, it may be better simply to leave the horse as he is. If he is treated quietly and calmly, and not upset, he may eventually accept clipping more easily.

Horses may become difficult to clip for a variety of reasons. The most common causes are connected with rough handling and lack of tact, and include:

Electric shock.

Over-heated blades.

Blunt blades.

Bruising and/or cutting by the machine.

Rough or impatient handling.

Clipping for too long a time without rest, especially the first time the horse is clipped.

Remedies

It can be helpful to stand a nervous horse within sight and hearing of another quiet horse who is being clipped.

Use a grooming machine to accustom him to the noise and vibration. However, some horses will not accept this.

Before attempting a lengthy clip, trim the horse so that he becomes used to the feel of the machine.

Music may have a calming effect, or cotton wool in the horse's ears may help.

The use of a small battery-driven clipper may be less worrying to the horse, as there is less noise and vibration. With such a small machine, it may not be possible to achieve a full clip because of over-heating.

When clipping difficult horses, any rough handling is self-defeating. Personnel involved should be calm, skilled, unhurried and sufficiently strong to hold the horse. It is an advantage if the person clipping is tall, as he can clip the horse's head with greater ease.

Sedation
It may be necessary to sedate a very difficult horse. In some cases, a total anaesthetic is required, when it will be necessary to take the horse to the surgery, or alternatively pay for the veterinary surgeon's waiting time while the animal is clipped. In most cases, if patience and kindness are used, these extreme measures may be avoided.

There can be problems connected with the use of sedatives on horses for the purpose of clipping. For the sedative to work satisfactorily the horse must be calm and unworried when it is administered. When administered by injection into a muscle, it may take from 30 to 40 minutes to take effect. The sedative may wear off before clipping is finished. In this event, the horse can quickly become violent and may cause injury to his holder or the person clipping. If he remains upset, clipping must be stopped. Re-sedation may not be possible until the next day. The horse should have only gentle exercise on the day following sedation.

TRIMMING

In winter, horses and ponies at grass should be left untrimmed, but in summer they may be trimmed in the same way as a stabled horse.

Whiskers
These can be removed to give a smart and tidy appearance. However, it should be remembered that they are the animal's chief means of feel. Many owners will not have them trimmed, as they are of particular use to grass-kept animals.

Ears
The long hair in the ears may be clipped level. To do this the ear is held closed up and the machine is used in a downwards direction from the tip of the ear to the base. The inside hair *should not be clipped*, because the internal hairs give protection from cold, dirt and infection. Grass-kept animals should not have their ears trimmed.

Cat Hairs
These are long hairs which grow a week or so after clipping, particularly in January and February. They may be removed by clipping lightly in the direction of the hair using a coarse blade.

A singeing lamp can be used, but it is now considered rather out of date since the development of modern clipping machines. It is a small flat metal holder containing a wick soaked in methylated spirit. It is set alight and then passed quickly over the body, singeing off any long hairs. It should not be used in a straw-bedded stable. The best place is a rubber-floored utility box or an enclosed and sheltered area in the yard. It should only be used by an experienced person who is aware both of the dangers of fire and of scorching the horse.

Heels and Fetlocks
In winter, these may be trimmed if necessary when the horse is clipped. In summer, well-bred horses may be trimmed by hand with a comb and sharp, blunt-ended scissors. The hair is raised by the comb and then trimmed off, so that there are no rough edges, in much the same way that human hair is cut by a good hairdresser. The operation requires practice and skill. Coarse-coated horses who grow

Clipping the ears.

heavy feather are more easily trimmed by machine. A coarse lower blade, called a leg plate, may be fitted. This tidies the hair, but does not clip too closely. Some horses grow very fine feather, which may be pulled out by hand.

In Mountain and Moorland show classes, native ponies and Welsh Cobs are left untrimmed. Arabs grow very little hair and are left untrimmed.

Jaw, Withers and Poll Piece
These need to be kept tidy throughout the year. Either the normal clipping machine may be used, or alternatively a lighter machine, similar to a dog clipper. This machine is also useful for trimming legs and ticklish, awkward parts of the horse. It is very light, easy to handle, and is quieter and vibrates less than a large clipping machine. Some types are battery powered. Chin hairs may also be pulled out by hand, but only a few each day. When trimming the poll and withers area, great care is needed to avoid the trimmed areas becoming larger and larger. Well-bred animals are often more neatly trimmed with scissors.

Hogging
This is the removal of the mane by clipping machine. In

former years hogging was very fashionable, but nowadays it is not often seen except on polo ponies. It saves labour, and is a means of keeping tidy a mane which has been rubbed, for instance because of sweet itch, or caught on wire. It is also used on some cobs and ponies.

To hog, the horse's head should be held low and stretched, so that a clean cut can be achieved. Use the clippers from the withers towards the poll. Once hogged, a mane may take up to two years to grow, and at first will be coarse and upright.

The mane is clipped once a week and cleaned daily with a damp brush.

PULLING THE MANE

This is done to:

Improve the appearance.

Thin out a thick mane.

Encourage the mane to lie flat.

Shorten a long mane.

Make the mane easier to plait.

Arrange to pull the mane after exercise, or on a warm day, when the pores of the skin are open. This makes the hairs easier to pull out, causing less discomfort to the horse. To avoid making the skin very sore, it may be advisable to spread the mane pulling over several days. Some horses have very thick manes, and these can be the toughest to pull. Well-bred horses usually have thinner manes. Care must be taken in this case that the mane is not made too short. Do not wash the mane before pulling, as this makes the hair soft and slippery and difficult to pull.

It is customary to encourage the mane to lie on the off side of the horse's neck. The manes of young horses may be trained to lie over by regular brushing, damping down and, when the horse is stabled, by loose plaiting. The manes of older horses are more difficult to retrain. If they lie on the near side and are tidy, they may be left.

The mane should never be shortened by cutting with scissors. This will leave an unsightly and very obvious edge. A very thin mane may be shortened by carefully breaking off the ends of the hair with the fingers. This leaves a natural looking edge. Clippers should not be used to thin a thick mane by cutting the underlying hair.

The manes and tails of all Arabs and Mountain and Moorland ponies, if they are to be shown in breed classes, are never pulled.

Method

☐ Thoroughly brush out the mane. A thick, tangled mane requires combing out. Remove the underneath hairs first and then shorten the top hairs. This should allow the mane to lie flat. It is a matter of preference as to whether a mane comb or a tail comb is used. Start at the poll, with the comb in the right hand. Take a few hairs

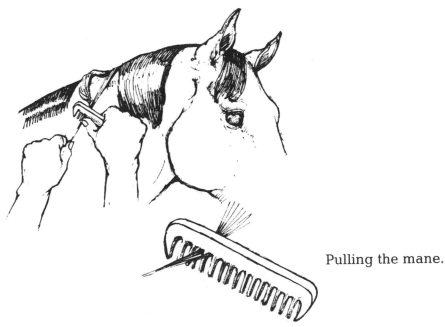

Pulling the mane.

Keeping the mane down.

in the left hand, run the comb up them to the roots, and then with a sharp firm pull, ease them out. The forelock is done last.

☐ When brushed out and dampened down, the mane should be about 10 to 12cm (4 to 5in) long. If it is still unruly, it may be encouraged to settle by tying a damp stable rubber round the horse's neck, and leaving it for several hours a day. Loose plaiting also helps.

PLAITING THE MANE

The mane is plaited to:

Make the horse look smart, for example for showing, competing and hunting, or when the horse is to be seen by prospective purchasers.

Train the unruly mane of a stabled horse. Plaiting for this purpose is done very loosely and the plaits are left long and not bundled up. They should be re-done each day. Rubber bands may be used. If the horse starts to rub the plaits, they should be undone and the mane should be washed.

Equipment for Plaiting

Comb (mane or tail), water brush, needle, thread of a colour to match the mane, scissors, bucket of water. If necessary, a metal feed bin or wooden box on which to stand.

Thread the needle and place it securely in a coat lapel. Needles are easily mislaid, which can be dangerous. If they are lost the surrounding bed should be removed, the floor swept and fresh bedding put down.

Method

☐ Start at the poll. Comb out the mane and dampen it down. With the comb, divide the mane evenly into as many plaits as are required. This varies according to personal preference, prevailing fashion, the length of the neck and the thickness of the mane. The appearance of a fat neck can be improved with a smaller number of tight, bunch plaits; a poorly developed neck can be improved by thick plaits which are not pulled too tight. In all cases it is customary to have an uneven number of plaits up the neck.

☐ Take the first section of hair, divide it into three and plait down as far as possible. Take the needle and thread and sew it firmly. Turn the plait under, stitch and then turn up again. Stitch each turn so that it is firm and there are

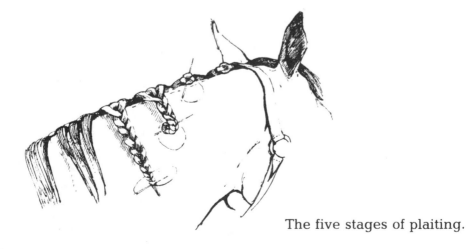

The five stages of plaiting.

no stray ends. The resultant plait should be button-like, preferably with no thread showing. Proceed down the neck. The two plaits in front of the withers require extra stitching, as there may be friction from the martingale, breastplate and reins. The forelock is done last.

☐ To achieve tidy and firm plaits it is essential to stand at an easy height. Short people may need a bale of straw or a strong box on which to stand.

☐ If time is short, rubber bands, of a colour which matches the mane, may be used instead of thread. They should never be used where correct turnout is expected. The rubber band is looped several times round the end of the plait. The plait is then bundled up, and the band looped round the whole plait until it is firm and tight.

☐ It is not advisable to plait manes the night before. Hay and bedding become embedded in the plaits, some hairs break and the result is untidy. Some horses try to rub out the plaits, with even worse results.

PULLING THE TAIL

The tail is pulled to:

Improve its appearance.

Show off the horse's quarters.

Save time when turning horses out for showing, competition, hunting, etc, when the tail must be either pulled or plaited. (It is better not to plait the tail the night before, for the same reasons as for mane plaiting.)

The tails of horses and ponies at grass should not be pulled, as the long hair protects the dock area.

Tail pulling should be done when the horse is warm and the pores of the skin open. Thoroughly brush out the tail, removing all tangles, but do not wash the top of the tail as this makes it slippery and difficult to pull. The procedure now varies according to the amount of hair to be removed. Well-bred horses should require only a small amount of hair to be removed from each side of the dock for about 15 to 20cm (6 to 8in). The centre portion can either be slightly shortened or pulled to match the sides.

Because the pulling causes discomfort and sometimes bleeding, it is preferable to take several days to complete it. The hair is removed by using the fingers, or with the help of a mane or tail comb. The hair is pulled out with a short sharp tug. After pulling, the tail should be washed and bandaged. Resin on the fingers will give a better purchase.

Horses who grow heavy tails need to have a lot of hair removed. Some sensitive horses object, and with these an assistant is needed to hold up a front leg. If the horse is still difficult, it is advisable to place an upended bale of straw in front of the person pulling. Alternatively, it is sometimes possible to hold the tail over a stable door and so complete the task. A twitch may help to control the horse (see Chapter 1). With very resentful animals, it may be more sensible simply to keep the tail well brushed and bandaged, and to plait it for special occasions.

Once a tail has been pulled, it should be kept tidy and well bandaged and the growing hair should be removed

A pulled and banged tail.

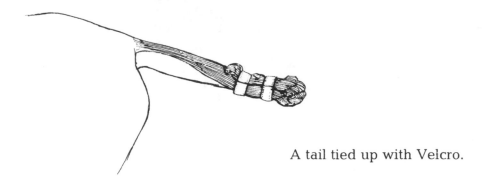

A tail tied up with Velcro.

regularly. If the hair of a pulled tail is allowed to grow, it will at first have a bushy and unsightly appearance.

When first learning to pull tails, it is helpful to have an experienced observer on hand. It is easy to pull out too much and to finish with a nearly bald dock.

PUTTING UP A TAIL

This is done so that in wet muddy conditions the horse's tail remains comparatively clean and dry. Eventers, polo ponies, and occasionally hunters have their tails put up to help keep them out of the way.

The upper part of the tail is usually pulled. The main portion is firmly plaited down to the end, where it may be either stitched or secured with a rubber band. The bottom half of the tail is doubled up underneath and secured by stitching, by tapes or by rubber bands. The latter, if too tight, may restrict circulation. Thread, tape and bands should match the tail in colour.

PLAITING THE TAIL

The tail should be washed and then well brushed out. There are two methods of plaiting: one with a flat plait and the other with a ridge plait. The latter requires more skill and practice.

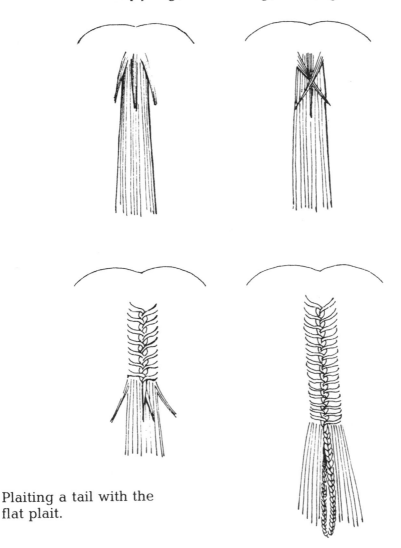

Plaiting a tail with the
flat plait.

Method

☐ From the top of the dock, take a few hairs from either
side and some from the centre. The centre strands can be
tied with thread. These are the three locks of hair which
make the plait. Plait them together and then work down
the tail, each time taking a few more hairs from the side.
No more hair is taken from the centre. Continue plaiting

95

approximately two-thirds of the way down the dock. From then on, continue plaiting without taking any more hair from the sides until the end of the plait is reached. The end of the plait is firmly stitched, and then doubled up underneath and again stitched.

☐ To achieve the flat plait, the locks of hair are brought inwards and passed one over the top of the other. To make a ridge plait, the locks of hair are passed from underneath, so that a ridge line is made on top. For the first method the finger nails face downwards and for the second they face upwards.

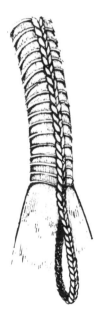

A ridge plait.

CHAPTER 6

Recognising Good Health and Caring for a Sick Horse

Condition is the bodily state of the horse. An experienced manager with a trained eye will be able to recognise the condition of all the horses in his care, and will be quick to observe any change.

SIGNS OF GOOD HEALTH

☐ A light, alert expression.

☐ Clear eyes. The membrane under the lids should be pale salmon pink in colour.

☐ No discharge from the eyes or nose.

☐ Mobile ears.

☐ A glossy coat which lies flat.

☐ Loose skin, which moves easily over the underlying bones.

☐ The horse stands with all four feet evenly on the ground or, if relaxed, one hind leg resting only.

☐ No visible sign of sweating when at rest, except in very hot weather or in humid conditions.

☐ Cool limbs, with no unusual swelling.

☐ Fairly thick and colourless or pale yellow urine, which should be passed several times a day.

☐ Droppings that are free from any offensive smell and are passed several times a day. They may be of various colour and consistency, according to the diet.

☐ Normal appetite and water consumption.

☐ A temperature of 38°C. (100.5°F.).

☐ A pulse rate at rest of 36 to 42 beats a minute.

☐ A respiration rate at rest of 8 to 12 inhalations a minute.

GRADES OF CONDITION

The Very Poor Horse

The animal is emaciated, with spine, ribs, tail, head and hip bones prominent. The bone structure of the backbone, withers, shoulders and neck are clearly visible. There is no fatty tissue under the skin, which feels tight over the bones and is not easily moved. The muscles of the shoulders, loins and quarters are underdeveloped and flaccid. The outline

Emaciated horse.

over the top of the quarters is hollow and falling away. The animal is often dehydrated, which is indicated by the slow recovery to normal of a fold of skin when pinched.

Horses in very poor condition are likely to be infected with worms, but such starved animals should be wormed with care (see Chapter 7, *Internal Parasites.*) Veterinary advice is essential. They are also likely to be infested with lice, which causes irritation, and bare patches of skin may be visible. Such animals require easily digested food in small quantities at frequent intervals. The quantity of food should be increased only gradually. Riding horses and ponies should not be worked until their condition has improved. This may take many weeks.

The Thin Horse
A thin horse is one with little fat between muscle and skin. The backbone and ribs are easily felt and visible. The skin is tight, but less so than in the very poor horse. The neck may be hard, but lacks substance. If such a horse is in work, there may be some muscle development, but if exercise is

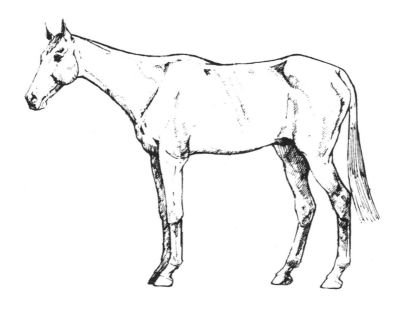

Thin horse.

reduced, muscles will waste and the loins and quarters will fall in. There is a risk of saddle sores developing.

In winter the appearance of ponies at grass can often be deceiving. They grow long thick coats, which may help to give an appearance of plumpness. They should be closely examined, particularly in the neck and backbone area, to make sure that they are in an acceptable condition.

A pony in good bodily condition usually grows a dense but not long winter coat. His summer coat is likely to come through earlier than that of a pony in poor condition. The latter often retains patches of long winter coat until well into the summer.

The Fit Horse
The backbone is not visible, and the flesh on either side is level. The ribs are barely distinguished, though they can just be felt. The shoulders and neck blend smoothly into body. The neck, when felt, is hard and has substance. The

Fit event horse.

skin over the ribs is loose and easily moved. The muscles are well developed and firm to the touch.

Four distinct categories of fitness can be recognised:

- *The ridden show animal.* Fairly well muscled up, but often overfat. Ribs not visible and can only just be felt.

- *The show jumper.* Well muscled, but may be quite fat. Ribs cannot be seen, but can be felt.

- *The event horse.* Very well muscled, but should not be carrying too much weight. Ribs can be seen and felt.

- *The racehorse.* Very well muscled but with no surplus fat. Muscles are rounded and can be clearly seen and felt, including above the bony points, especially over the loins and croup. There is little fat in the spaces between muscles. This horse, to an uneducated eye, may appear thin.

The Plump Horse
Fat deposits can be felt over and between the ribs and along the withers, shoulders and neck. The crest feels

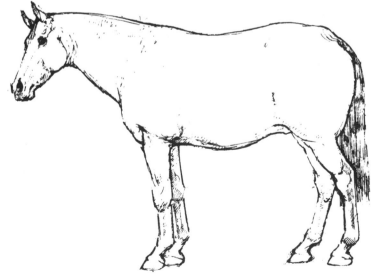

Fat horse.

solid. Food must be restricted and no fast work undertaken. This condition is typical of horses, and particularly ponies, turned out on good grazing in the summer.

The Fat Horse
The fat horse has fat deposits on either side of his backbone. His ribs cannot be felt. There is fat in the areas around the withers behind the shoulders, along the inner thighs and around the tail and head. The crest feels thick and solid.

The Very Fat Horse
The very fat horse has an obvious crease down his back. His ribs are covered with a layer of fat and cannot be felt. There is bulging fat around his tail, head, withers, shoulders and neck. His flank is filled with fat, and his crest very thick and solid.

In the last two cases there is an urgent need to restrict severely the horse's food. The extra weight is a health hazard to heart, wind and legs. Laminitis must be imminent, if not already apparent. Animals in such condition may be said to be equally as neglected as those who are allowed to become too thin. Exercise is advisable, but should be limited to walking – hill work should be avoided.

SICK NURSING AND THE CONTROL OF INFECTION

At all times the attendant must be observant and must use common sense to ensure the horse's welfare. Close attention must be paid to comfort, cleanliness and diet. The veterinary surgeon's instructions should be written down and carefully followed.

Stable
A very sick horse may well settle and be more peaceful if he is put in a loosebox in a quiet or separate part of the yard.

However, some horses become upset if they are required to change boxes, and are better left in their own environment where they have company. Horses with eye trouble should have light restricted and smaller windows and the top-door openings should be covered. Essential ventilation must be maintained.

Warmth

In cold weather, or in some forms of illness, warmth is essential, which should be achieved by using extra lightweight clothing, rather than by restricting ventilation. There must be an ample supply of fresh air; the atmosphere in the box must never feel stuffy. Outside looseboxes may have the top door closed, providing there is another adequate form of draught-proof ventilation. Stable bandages, warm, lightweight blankets and, on occasions, a hood, all help to combat the cold. An infra-red lamp fixed in the ceiling adds to the horse's comfort. This can usually be run from a suitable light fixture if no permanent socket is available.

In warm weather there must be an ample supply of fresh air but no draughts. Light rugs may be put on, but care must be taken that the horse does not become overheated, as excessive warmth can be damaging. A sweat rug may be used during the day, and a night rug put on when the temperature falls in the evening.

Bedding

An ample bed, with banked up walls, should be provided. It should be kept clean and regularly skipped out. A weak or injured horse's leg may become entangled in deep straw, so this type of bedding should be well flattened and not shaken up unnecessarily. If shavings or paper are used, the problem is avoided and there is also less disturbance and dust when the bed is mucked out. Shavings or sawdust are not suitable when a wound has to be left uncovered, or during foaling.

In the case of very sick horses, grooming should be restricted. The eyes, nose, sheath and dock area should be sponged clean, and the horse may perhaps appreciate a light body brush or hand rubbing over his head and body. Stable bandages should be removed twice a day, and the legs hand rubbed towards the heart. The feet should always be carefully picked out. A clean cotton sheet worn under the rugs can make a horse more comfortable. In the case of infections or contagious diseases, grooming should be discontinued, as brushing can only assist the spread of the infection. In cases of lameness, or in convalescence, a thorough grooming can be beneficial and is usually enjoyed by the horse.

Hygiene
In cases of infectious or contagious disease, stable tools, grooming equipment and food utensils should all be kept separate. The attendant should wear a special overall, headgear and rubber gloves when looking after the horse. A bucket of strong disinfectant should be kept outside the door for washing boots. Jeyes Fluid is suitable.

Water
A constant supply of clean, fresh water must be available. In all cases where the horse's water intake has to be monitored, automatic watering bowls should be disconnected and water supplied by bucket. All water containers must be cleaned out and filled with water several times a day. This is particularly important where there are nasal discharges.

Diet
In all cases a low concentrate diet will be necessary. If possible it should be based on the one which the horse is used to, with the forage level being increased and the concentrate level decreased. It should include nutritious and easily digestible ingredients. Soaked sugar beet, bread meal with chaff or molassed chaff, plus hay or vacuum-packed forage would provide an open yet balanced diet. Meadow hay is

easier to chew and to digest than seed hay and horses with respiratory diseases are best fed from the ground, with the feed damped and the hay soaked. Fresh-cut grass makes a suitable and appetising ration. Apples, carrots or other roots may also tempt the appetite.

It is essential to appreciate the preferences and needs of the particular animal. All food should be freshly prepared and offered in small quantities. In some cases, hand feeding may be necessary. Uneaten food should be removed after half an hour and discarded.

Feed bowls and mangers should be washed out after every feed.

For special cases the veterinary surgeon may suggest a suitable diet.

Administration of Medicines
If medicines are mixed in feeds or· added to the water, they may put the horse off his food or discourage him from drinking. It is better to mix them with water and· administer them by syringe into the mouth, or mix them with treacle and put this on the tongue (see Chapter 1, *Handling the Horse*).

Routine Care
The horse's temperature, pulse and respiration should be taken morning and night and noted on a chart. This chart should also contain information as to the state of the dung and urine, how often they are passed, and also details of water consumption, food eaten and the horse's appetite.

In epidemic situations it is sensible to chart the temperatures of all horses in the yard morning and night.

The normal temperature of a horse is 38°C. (100.5°F.). There can be slight variations from horse to horse.

To take the temperature
The horse should be held by an assistant. Sharp horses

should have a front leg held up. The thermometer should be the type with a short stubby end. Shake it until it registers below 37°C. (99.5°F.). Grease it with Vaseline and, standing to the side of the horse's quarters, insert two-thirds of it into the rectum. Leave it for half a minute, or as directed. The thermometer should be firmly held, as it can be drawn into the rectum and be difficult to recover. After taking it out and noting the reading, shake the thermometer down, wash it in cool disinfectant, dry it and replace it in its case.

To take the pulse
The normal pulse of a horse at rest is 36 to 42 beats to the minute. The pulse can be taken by a light feel of the artery as it crosses the horse's jaw bone. It is a skill which needs practice. It is helpful to have a watch with a second hand and a large, easily seen face.

Respiratory rate
The normal respiration of a horse at rest is 8 to 12 inhalations per minute. This can be observed by watching the movement of the horse's flank.

Control of Infection and Contagion
It must be accepted that in many cases it is not possible to prevent the spread of airborne germs, or to stop other horses from becoming infected. The offending animal may be contagious for several days before showing any signs of illness. In any case, an isolation box is unlikely to be of use unless it is at least 400 metres ($^1/_4$ mile) downwind from the yard. Birds and flies also carry germs.

Isolation boxes should be used for housing animals new to the yard, particularly those bought from sales or any who have travelled long distances.

Precautions Which Can Be Taken:
☐ The person attending the horse should not be in contact with any other horses.

106

☐ The veterinary surgeon should see other patients in the yard before seeing the infectious horse.

☐ Overall washing facilities and paper towels should be provided.

☐ A grille over the door prevents any passer-by from handling the horse and helps to prevent airborne infection.

☐ A warning notice should be pinned to the door.

☐ A supply of paper towels and cotton wool should be available for dealing with nasal discharge.

☐ Used material should be burned. Rubber gloves should be disinfected after use, or plastic disposable gloves used.

☐ In the case of contagious skin diseases, for example, ringworm, the most likely points of infection and contact should be carefully watched on all other horses, for example the girth, saddle and bridle areas and where the rider's leg rests. Early signs of the disease can thus be noted and treatment given before it spreads. All riders should disinfect their boots before riding another horse.

☐ Horses with ringworm may be rideable. They should have their tack kept separate, and this should be disinfected each day. If numnahs and nylon tack are used, disinfection is easier and leather saddlery will not be harmed. Attendants and riders should bath each day, and if possible wash their hair. Special soap can be obtained. Particular attention should be paid to any place where there is friction from clothing, for instance the wrists, neck, etc.

Convalescence
A horse who has had a serious illness may need several months convalescence before being fit to work. Exercise may start with five minutes walking out and progress

gradually as the horse gains strength. When work is resumed, it should progress in very slow stages, so that at no time is the horse put under strain.

The veterinary surgeon will advise as to a suitable programme.

The horse must be kept warm without being over-heated. Hill work of any sort should be avoided. Walking on long reins can give more control and less strain than lungeing. Work on a circle can put undue pressure on slack muscles.

Cleaning and Disinfecting Stables and Equipment

☐ Competition and racing yards usually employ professional cleaning services, and the buildings concerned can be steam cleaned. This is an expensive process, and the private owner or the small yard is more likely to do the work personally.

☐ To remove grease and dirt, use washing soda and bleach. Used together these are also an effective disinfectant, and kill fungus. A strong disinfectant, such as Jeyes Fluid or Lysol, also kills fungus.

☐ The Jockey Club recommends Halamid. The Ministry of Agriculture recommends creoline derivatives (synthetic Phonolee disinfectant, for example Hycolin).

☐ All bedding should be removed and burned.

☐ The roof or ceiling should be washed down with a jet hose to remove all dust. The walls, doors (inside and out), windows, mangers and doors should be scrubbed clean with washing soda and bleach. When dry, unpainted woodwork can be creosoted.

☐ Brick or block walls may be Snowcemmed or emulsion painted.

☐ Clothing and grooming kit should be soaked in disinfectant (not bleach or soda) for six hours, then washed in detergent and carefully rinsed.

☐ Stable tools, buckets and portable mangers should be washed with strong washing soda and bleach.

☐ Leather saddlery which has been in contact with a fungal infection (for example, ringworm) should first be cleaned with washing soda and water, then with a strong disinfectant. It can then be oiled. Soda is bad for leather, but a daily application of glycerine soap should soon restore it. Non-leather girths, numnahs and nylon tack should be soaked in strong disinfectant (Jeyes Fluid or Lysol) for six hours and then washed.

POULTICES

Poultices may be used warm or cold, and can be applied anywhere on the horse where they can successfully be kept in place.

Warm Poultices

☐ Soften the tissues, so that pus can escape.

☐ Increase the blood supply to the injured area, and thus assist healing.

☐ Soothe bruising.

Warm poulticing should be put on at blood heat.

Cold Poultices

☐ Reduce inflammation.

☐ Constrict blood vessels and arrest internal haemorrhage.

As a basic principle, cold poultices are for immediate use to ease inflammation; warm poultices are for foot infections, deep puncture wounds and to help the healing process once the original inflammation has subsided. Poultices are usually left on for twenty-four hours and then removed. The poulticing of wounds on a joint, particularly the knee, should be done only on veterinary advice.

Types of Poultices

Kaolin is a natural clay with medicinal properties. It may be applied warm or cold. It can be used on open wounds, but is better encased in muslin. It is used for bruising, strains and all foot injuries.

Animalintex is a prepared medicinal lint. It is applied warm or cold. It is used where there is an open wound, or for a punctured foot. It has less of a clogging effect than kaolin.

Glycerine and Epsom Salts mixed to a paste may be applied cold, and are of particular value for coronet abscesses and swollen cannons.

Bran and Epsom Salts 227g (½lb) bran and 57 to 85g (2 to 3oz) of Epsom salts are mixed with hot water to form a stiff dough which is used for foot problems.

Yeast is applied cold.

Bran and Epsom salts, and yeast, may be used for foot injuries. They soften the sole of the foot or heel area, and encourage pus to escape. However, there can be a problem with the bran poultice. The horse may be tempted to pull off the covering and eat it. To deter this, mix it with strong disinfectant.

Method

Leg Poultice

Kaolin. If applied warm, kaolin has to be heated in its tin or in a small container in a saucepan of boiling water. The lid should be eased so that steam can escape. The water must

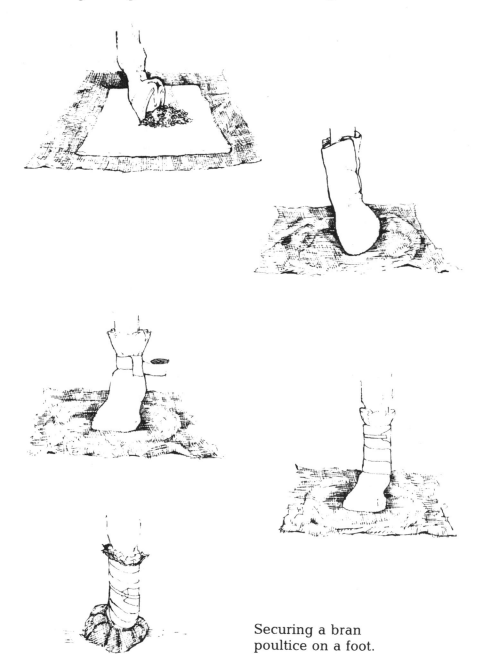

Securing a bran
poultice on a foot.

not be so deep that it can overflow into the tin. To test for temperature, stir well and then test a small portion on the back of the hand to ensure that it is not too hot. An over-hot poultice will blister the horse's skin. Kaolin may also be heated by spreading it approximately 6mm (¼ in) thick on a suitable sized piece of cotton or linen. This is then put on a flat container and placed either in an oven or under a grill on a low heat. It heats very quickly, and care should be taken that it does not dry out.

If kaolin is heated in a tin, the poultice is then spooned out on to a suitable sized piece of plastic, tin foil or brown paper. Test it again for heat and then place it on the injury; cover with thick Gamgee and secure with a stable or crêpe bandage. This must be firm, but not tight. If the kaolin has previously been spread on cloth, this is placed on the injury, covered with plastic and Gamgee and bandaged as above. The purpose of the plastic is to keep in the heat, exclude air and retain moisture, thus allowing the poultice to work.

Animalintex. A suitably sized piece of lint is cut off and placed on a plate or other clean surface. The lint is then saturated with boiling water. The surplus is removed either by placing another plate of equal size over it and squeezing, or by placing it in a clean cloth and squeezing. Test the lint for heat on the back of the hand and apply directly to the injury, dressing side down. The lint is covered and kept in place in a similar way to kaolin (the plastic covering is essential). It can also be used as a dry poultice, or dampened with water if applied cold (see instructions on packet).

Glycerine and Epsom salts. The paste is placed over the wound, covered with plastic and bandaged, as for kaolin.

Yeast. The foot is packed with unheated yeast and covered as for a kaolin poultice.

Foot Poultice
All surfaces of the foot should be scrubbed clean. Using an

Equi Boot the selected poultice is placed over the area of the foot to be treated. Plastic is put on top and the Equi Boot then put on and secured to the foot. If the boot fits well, it is sometimes possible to allow the animal to be turned out.

Using a poultice boot. The poultice is put on as above. Bran or Epsom salts or yeast may be used instead. Place the poultice over the sole of the foot, cover with plastic, place the foot in the poultice boot and fasten securely. The leg should be protected with Gamgee and a stable bandage. The heel of the foot, if not the seat of injury, should be protected by a layer of thick grease.

Using a thick plastic bag and/or sack. The selected poultice is either placed on the sole of the foot or, if it is bran based, is placed in the bottom of a strong plastic bag. The foot is then placed in the bag, which may be covered with sacking. This is then wrapped round the fetlock and leg. The leg should be protected with Gamgee. The sack and/or bag can be tied round the pastern with an old crêpe bandage or string. A stockinette bandage is then put on to secure the Gamgee and the top of the sack or plastic bag. This is made more secure by putting on a stable bandage. With heavyweight horses it may be necessary to reinforce the bag or sack. The pressure of weight quickly wears through a thin layer of sacking or plastic.

Cold kaolin poultice. This should be chilled in a refrigerator before use. It can be applied with advantage to all four legs of a horse after any type of severe work. The kaolin is put on the leg by hand, then covered with brown paper and thick Gamgee. A secure, but not tight, stable bandage is then put on. Various forms of prepared bandage for use as a cold poultice are now available.

Inflamed backs under the saddle. Inflammation can be reduced by putting cold kaolin on the area and covering it with plastic. This can be held in place by Elastoplast.

Note: Both warm and cold kaolin eventually return to blood heat.

In all cases of leg or foot injury, thick Gamgee and a support bandage should be placed on the opposite leg to prevent filling and to ease strain.

Knee and hock bandages. Apply the dressing or poultice as directed, and cover all surfaces of the joint with thick Gamgee. With the knee, it is the bony surface at the back of the joint, and with the hock, the bony surface at the front of the joint, which may become bruised and sore from friction and pressure when the joint is moved.

The bandage, preferably crêpe, is started below the joint with two secure rounds. It is then put round the joint in a figure-of-eight pattern, leaving either the back of the knee or the front of the hock free. It should finish below the joint. There is little friction from this type of bandage. A stable bandage should be placed on the leg below the joint to prevent the upper bandage slipping down.

Putting on knee and hock bandages requires considerable skill and experience. It is advisable to practise beforehand, so that should the necessity arise the bandaging itself will cause no problem.

Horses often attempt to chew at a knee covering, especially over a wound (see Chapter 1).

Various patented forms of leg support and protection are now available, some of which can usefully be used to retain poultices and dressings, particularly on awkward areas such as the knee or hock.

Pressure bandage. This type of bandage is used after a suspected tendon injury. The bandage helps to limit any swelling caused by the injury. Such swelling interferes with the healing process. The bandage, preferably crêpe, should be put on over a thick layer of evenly applied Gamgee. It should be removed each morning and night, and the leg should be given a brisk massage by hand, the hands working in an upward direction towards the heart.

TUBBING

This is useful for puncture wounds in the foot. It draws out pus without softening the horn.

Method

- ☐ Scrub the foot clean.
- ☐ Use a clean container of heavy-duty plastic or rubber. The handle should be removed.
- ☐ Dissolve 227g (8oz) of Epsom salts in hot water.
- ☐ Place the Epsom salts and water in the container and reduce to blood heat.
- ☐ Place the horse's foot in the container and soak for ten minutes. Top up with water if required.

Repeat three or four times a day.

FOMENTING

This is a method of applying heat to areas which cannot be poulticed.

Method

- ☐ Dissolve 227g (8oz) of Epsom salts in hot water.
- ☐ Place the Epsom salts and water in a bucket and reduce to blood temperature.
- ☐ Soak an old towel in the water, wring it out and apply to the affected area.
- ☐ Repeat every minute and continue for fifteen to twenty minutes. Top up with hot water as required.

COLD HOSING

This treatment is appropriate for the immediate relief of

Fomenting a forearm.

bruising, for instance following a kick, or a bang when jumping.

Method

☐ Ask an assistant to hold the horse, who may need to be bridled for extra control.

☐ Run the water gently over the foot at minimum pressure.

☐ Gradually work up the leg to the bruised area, and allow a slight increase of water pressure.

☐ Continue the treatment for ten minutes, and repeat four or five times during the day.

☐ An alternative, if available, is to stand the horse in a running stream or in the sea.

☐ Pressure bandages, if practicable, should be applied between hosing sessions.

COLD BANDAGES

Patented forms of cold pack are now available. Makers' instructions should be followed. These packs can be held in place on the leg with a light bandage. Gamgee, or something similar, should be placed underneath the bandage.

An ice pack can be made by crushing ice cubes in a cloth and placing them in a plastic bag. Cover the leg with Gamgee, or similar, and put the ice bag on the leg and secure with Gamgee or a light bandage.

CHAPTER 7
Internal Parasites

'Worms' is the common name given to an important group of internal parasites of the horse. All horses and ponies, except new born foals, may suffer from worms.

Worms cause anaemia, debility, unthriftiness and colic. This means that horses are not able to work up to their true potential, food is wasted and young horses do not grow properly. Almost 90 per cent of all colic cases can be traceable to worm infestation. In some cases they lead to death.

A proper routine to control worms is, therefore, an essential part of any horse-care programme. Money spent on wormers (anthelmintics) is excellent insurance for cheerful, healthy horses and ponies, who can enjoy their work and give of their best.

SYMPTOMS OF WORMS

The following symptoms should be cause for concern, although some may occur for other reasons:

The horse eats well but puts on no condition.

He has a large belly but very little condition along his top line.

His skin feels dry and inelastic.

He is anaemic.

He has little energy and tires quickly.

His droppings are loose and smelly; sometimes there may be diarrhoea.

He has recurring attacks of colic.

NB: It is possible for horses and ponies to have a serious worm burden without visible outward signs.

SAMPLING OF FAECES

The harmful effects of the worms may have occurred before they can be diagnosed. Therefore, one negative worm count may mean nothing. In doubtful cases, regular counts must be taken. As long as most samples are negative, with possibly a few counts from 50 to 100 eggs per gram of dung, then the measures being taken against worms have been effective.

LIFE CYCLE

The life cycle of many worms are similar:

The eggs or larvae of most worms are taken in (ingested) by the horse during grazing.

Immature larvae migrate through the horse's body tissues.

Worms reach the 'predilection site' in different organs for different parasites and there mature.

Eggs or larvae from these mature worms are passed out in the faeces (dung).

Outside the horse, the worms develop to the stage when, if ingested by the horse, the cycle starts again.

119

Internal Parasites

MEASURE OF CONTROL

The worming of all horses, ponies and donkeys, especially those living at grass, should be carried out on a regular basis. *All* animals should be dosed every four to six weeks. It is a false economy to cut back on worming, especially with young animals.

Some parasites can build up a resistance to the group of Benzimidazole drugs. It is therefore sensible to change to an unrelated drug such as Ivermectin or Pyrantel every six months. If the wormer being used does not control bots (see *Methods of Dosing*, page 124) then either an organo-phosphorus compound or Ivermectin should be given once during the winter (see *bots*, page 122).

Foals are particularly susceptible to worm damage, as they have little immunity. This damage, apart from stunting their growth or even killing them, may affect them throughout their working lives. They should be dosed every month from six weeks onwards with an anthelmintic safe for foals and effective against *parascaris equorum*.

As grass is the commonest method of access for worms, the importance of clean grazing cannot be over-emphasised. Cross-grazing, preferably with cattle but also with sheep, especially during the spring and summer, helps reduce its population of infective larvae on the grass.

The daily picking up of droppings in small paddocks reduces the chances of infestation and increases the amount of palatable grass.

Resting the fields for several months or taking a crop of hay from them also reduces infestation.

All new horses should be routinely dosed and kept in for seventy-two hours before being turned out.

Even one untreated horse can contaminate the pasture and cause reinfection of his companions.

120

At present, nothing is known which can be put on grassland to kill the eggs or larvae.

MAIN TYPES OF INTERNAL PARASITES

Strongyles (redworms) are the most serious and dangerous group of all internal parasites affecting the horse. They can be divided into two types – large and small. The large are *strongylus vulgaris* and *strongylus edentatus*. The small strongyles, of which there are several species, are known as *trichonema*.

Strongylus vulgaris. The predilection site is the large intestine. The larvae on the pasture are eaten and travel through the walls of the intestine into the small blood vessels and then to the cranial mesenteric artery. Larvae develop here, then return to the intestine to develop to the adult stage and to produce eggs, which are excreted in the dung. The presence of larvae in this important artery can cause clinical symptoms which include fever, loss of appetite, recurrent colic and chronic diarrhoea. The outcome can be fatal.

Strongylus edentatus. Again, the predilection site is the large intestine, but the larvae migrate through the liver; this damages the liver but causes no specific symptoms.

Small stronglyes (trichonema). The predilection site is the large intestine. The larvae on the pasture are eaten, they migrate into the wall of the intestine and then move out into the gut and develop to maturity. Eggs are then produced, which are passed on to the pasture in the dung to develop into infective larvae.

Control
Control for all strongyles is the same. Most broad-spectrum anthelmintics kill adult worms and larval stages in the

gut, but Ivermectin, Oxfendazole and Fenbendazole (at increased dose rates) also kill the migrating larvae.

Parascaris equorum (roundworms)   These are most common in foals and yearlings. The predilection site is the small intestine. The eggs are deposited in stables and pasture. They can live for many years and are resistant to most chemical disinfectants. The eggs are taken in by the mouth during suckling from a contaminated teat, from udder skin or when grazing. The eggs hatch in the intestines; the larvae penetrate the gut wall and enter the lymph stream, travelling through the liver and then via the blood to the heart and the lungs, then into the airways to the throat and so back to the small intestine.

Symptoms
Unthriftiness, emaciation, dry staring coat, pot belly.
Sometimes there is an unexplained respiratory illness and coughing.

Control
All common anthelmintic drugs are effective. Foals should be treated from six weeks of age every four weeks with a wormer safe for foals.

Gasterophilus species (bots).   The predilection site of these larvae of horse bot flies is the stomach. The female fly lays eggs on the hairs of the horse's legs. They cause irritation and, when licked by the horse, hatch and migrate to the stomach. They are passed out in the dung as mature larvae which pupate and develop into flies during the summer.

Control
Ivermectin or an organophosphorus drug should be given in one annual dose. The directions on the organophosphorus drugs should be very carefully followed, as these can be dangerous. The droppings after dosing may prove fatal to birds. If eggs are seen on the legs during the summer,

they can be inactivated by washing vigorously with warm water containing an insecticide; alternatively they may be shaved off.

Strongyloides westeri (threadworms). The predilection site is the small intestine. These parasites can be free-living, especially in warm humid conditions such as a deep litter bed. They are of importance in foals. Infection can occur by two different routes. First, and most common, is via the dam's milk. The second is through penetration of the skin.

Symptoms
There is persistent scouring in the foal after the foal heat. The mare is simply a carrier of infection and shows no clinical signs.

Control
The stables should be kept clean and dry. With very young infected foals, veterinary help should be sought. Thiabendazole or Ivermectin are the usual drugs used. It is very difficult, if not impossible, to control the larvae in the mare and therefore the resultant infection in the foal.

Oxyuris equi (pinworms). The predilection site is the large intestine. The eggs containing larvae are taken in by mouth. These hatch and the worms develop in the wall of the large intestine before returning to the lumen of the gut. When mature, the female moves to the anus to lay her eggs.

Symptoms
Due to the irritation caused by the egg-laying females, the horse rubs the top of the tail and sometimes breaks the skin. Similar signs are seen in sweet itch and louse infestation.

Control
The treatment for other worms also deals with pinworms. The eggs should be washed off from under the tail with a disposable cloth.

Dictyocaulus arnfieldi (lungworms).   The predilection site is the major airways of the lungs. Lungworms are particularly common in donkeys, who are the main carriers of infection, although they may show no symptoms. The larvae are taken in from pasture and migrate through the lymphatic and blood system to the lungs. Mature worms produce larvae which then pass up the throat, are swallowed and hence excreted in the dung to develop to the infective stage on pasture. In horses over a year old the worms remain small and immature, and do not produce larvae, which makes diagnosis from the dung impossible. This is not so in foals and donkeys, where infection can frequently be diagnosed by finding larvae in the dung.

Symptoms
These only show in horses over one year old. A horse develops a persistent, chronic cough. Often, diagnosis is retrospective, after a favourable response to treatment with an anthelmintic effective against lungworm.

Control
Donkeys should be routinely treated in the spring. A single dose of Ivermectin, or twice the normal dose of Mebendazole for five days running, has been found effective. Treatment of horses may prove difficult, and veterinary advice should be sought. Increased doses of Fenbendazole have proved effective in clinical cases, and recent experimental work has shown that Ivermectin may be a useful drug against lungworms.

METHODS OF DOSING

Powder
Granules } are all added to feed
Pellets
Paste in a dosing syringe
Suspension

Active Principles of Anthelmintics
It is very important to read the name of the active principle as well as the trade name, so that the correct anthelmintic is used.

Benzimidazole Group
The advantages of this group of drugs are that they are of a broad spectrum, that is, they deal with many species of worms, and they are very safe. However, resistance to the whole group may be caused by using one of these drugs exclusively over a long period. There should be a change every six months.

The present range includes:

Thiabendazole

Mebendazole

Fenbendazole

Oxfendazole

Oxibendazole

Febantel

NOTE: This group of drugs is not effective against bots.

Ivermectin
This is a broad-spectrum drug, which also kills bots. It is unrelated to the Benzimidazole group.

Pyrantel
This is a broad-spectrum drug which, like Ivermectin, has the advantage that it is not related to the Benzimidazole group. It has no activity against bots.

Organophosphates
These can be dangerous drugs if directions are not carefully followed. They include Dichlorvos, which is the only broad-spectrum drug in the group. It is also effective against bot larvae. Other drugs in this group include Metriphonate and Haloxon, which are mainly used against bots.

125

FREQUENCY OF DOSING

The interval between treatments recommended for routine parasite control programmes is four to eight weeks. For this period the dung will be free of eggs so that further pasture contamination is prevented. With some of the older anthelmintics the period was four weeks, but with some of the modern Benzimidazoles and Ivermectin drugs this can be extended to six to eight weeks. Veterinary advice should be sought for a control programme which suits the particular situation.

CHAPTER 8
Shoeing

MODERN SHOEING PRACTICE

Horseshoeing has been an organised craft in Britain since 1356, when the Worshipful Company of Farriers was established in the City of London.

The Farriers Registration Act (1975) states that shoes can only be fitted to horses by persons registered to do so. Registration is confined to persons who have taken and passed the examinations of the Worshipful Company of Farriers (Registered Shoeing Smith until 1977 – now Diploma of the Worshipful Company of Farriers), or persons who at the time of the Act were practising farriery, either on their own or on other persons' horses, with or without reward.

An Apprentice Training Scheme was introduced by the Company in 1960. It is currently administered by the Farriers Registration Council and funded by the Council for Small Industries in Rural Areas. Apprenticeship is for four years, during which the apprentice attends for twenty-seven weeks the School of Farriery at Hereford Technical College, for theoretical and practical instruction.

There are some 2000 persons on the Register of Farriers, including about 300 registered to shoe their own horses. Some farriers operate from a forge to trim and hot shoe horses brought to them, but many others travel around their area. Factory-made shoes are available in many sizes, and are finished to a high standard. They save the craftsman many hours of work at the fire and anvil, and are an acceptable substitute for hand-made shoes. The key to successful shoeing is regular and correct trimming of the hooves to maintain the correct length and angle.

The modern farrier is a skilled craftsman. It is the responsibility of the owner to:

Make regular appointments for attention to his horse's feet.

Provide a clean, well-lit place with a level floor and protection from the weather.

Ensure that the horse is trained to stand quietly for trimming and shoeing.

BASIC STRUCTURE OF THE FOOT

Internal Structure
The bones in the foot are:

The first phalanx (long pastern bone).

The second phalanx (short pastern bone).

The third phalanx (pedal bone).

The navicular bone.

Tendons run down the leg and are attached to the bones, the superficial and deep flexor tendons at the back and the extensor at the front. The former flex the joints, the latter raise and extend the limb.

Ligaments hold the tendons and bones in place but at the same time allow necessary movement.

The lateral cartilages extend from the wings of the pedal bone towards the heels and form elastic shock absorbers.

The fleshy structures are tough elastic pads consisting of:

The plantar cushion or sensitive frog, which lies at the back of the foot.

The coronary band, which is a strip extending round the coronet from which the hoof grows.

The fleshy sole, which lies beneath the pedal bone.

The sensitive laminae cover the outer surface of the pedal bone, and form a junction between the fleshy and horny parts of the hoof. The fleshy structure and the sensitive laminae supply nutrition to their corresponding parts of the foot.

The foot is well supplied with *blood vessels* and *nerves*.

External Structure

The *hoof* forms a non-vascular and insensitive covering for the internal parts of the foot. It consists of the wall, the sole and the frog.

The wall is that part of the hoof which is visible when the foot is on the ground. It is more or less semi-circular, the front feet being rounder in shape than the hind feet. At the extremity of the *heels* it bends sharply back to form the *bars*. The area between the wall and the bars is called the *seat of corn*. The wall is thicker at the toe than at the heels, and expands slightly at the heel when the foot takes weight. It grows from the *coronary band*, and takes an average of nine to twelve months before coming into wear at the toe, and about six months at the heel. When working on hard surfaces, the wall cannot grow fast enough to replace the wear and shoeing is necessary.

The periople forms a shiny protective layer on the surface of the wall. It prevents undue evaporation; its removal by unnecessary rasping can cause the feet to become brittle owing to excessive loss of moisture. The water content

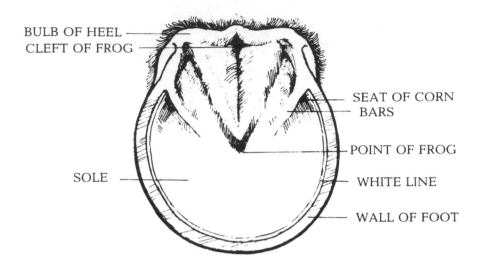

BULB OF HEEL
CLEFT OF FROG
SEAT OF CORN
BARS
POINT OF FROG
SOLE
WHITE LINE
WALL OF FOOT

Parts of the foot.

varies from 25 per cent in the wall to 40 per cent in the frog.

The junction between the wall and the sole is marked by a distinct *white line*. This forms an important guide to the farrier as to the thickness of the wall covering the sensitive laminae. It also marks the union between the sole and the wall.

The horny sole forms the bottom surface of the hoof. It is softer than the wall, and grows from the fleshy sole. Natural exfoliation maintains a constant thickness to the sole, but its shape and thickness vary between different horses.

The frog is of a tough elastic consistency. It is triangular in shape, and fits into the space between the angle of the heels. The depression in the centre is called the *cleft*. When the foot comes to the ground, the foot expands, acting both as a shock absorber and a weight-bearing surface. This expansion followed by contraction has an important function in maintaining the circulation of the blood in the foot.

CONFORMATION

Good or Normal Feet

The front foot should be rounder at the toe than the hind foot, and viewed from the side should usually make an angle with the ground of between 45° and 50°. Although the angle should be the same as the pastern axis, it may vary between horses. The inside wall is normally slightly steeper than the outside wall. The line when the foot is picked up should be symmetrical around an imaginary central mid-line. The heels should be wide apart and the frog large and well developed, with a definite cleft. This should not extend up between the heels. The sole should be slightly concave. Both feet should match in shape and size.

The hind foot is normally narrower and more upright than the front foot, with the toe less rounded. The angle with the ground should be between 50° and 55°. The sole is more concave, and the frog smaller. The feet should match.

The surface of the wall may have a number of rings. These are normally insignificant in size, and merely indicate changes in diet. But they may be large, in which case they could indicate a previous illness.

Some horses have unusually high heels. This may be the natural conformation of the feet, or it can be the result of the

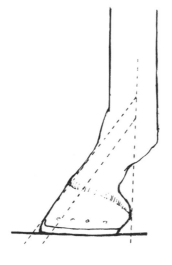

Well-balanced near forefoot.

way in which they are shod. Any excessive lowering of the heel, especially without corresponding cutting back of the toe to maintain the straight foot/pastern axis, can cause problems.

When the horse is standing naturally, all feet should point directly to the front. Any deviation affects both the movement of the leg and the wear of the shoe. Pigeon-toed or 'toed-in' horses show excessive wear of the outer branch of the shoe, those with 'toes out' produce extra wear on the inner branch.

The Pastern/Foot Axis
It is important to consider the balance of the foot with regard to the relationship between the slope of the pastern and the slope of the hoof wall. To ensure cranio-caudel (forward to backward) balance, the slopes should be similar. It is also important to maintain lateral to medial (side to side) balance, which ensures that the foot lands level on the ground. If the pastern/foot axis is broken back, for example by excessive length of the toe or by excessive lowering of the heels, undue strain is applied to the flexor tendons and suspensory apparatus of the distal limbs. Any imbalance will furthermore apply undue strain to the bones, joints and ligaments of both limbs.

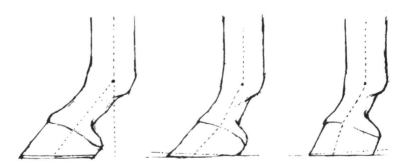

(*left*) Long sloping pastern. Foot axis maintained. Balance maintained. (*centre*) Toe too long. Foot axis not maintained. (*right*) Upright pastern. Foot axis not maintained. Balance not maintained.

Poor or Abnormal Feet

Flat feet show a decreased angle of the foot with the ground. The heels are low and the sole flat and often thin. The frog compensates for the poor conformation of the rest of the foot, and is usually large and well developed. Such feet are likely to sustain bruising of the sole and if they are not carefully shod, they are susceptible to corns.

Boxy or upright feet show an increased angle of the foot to the ground. The heels are high, the frog small and the horn texture is often very strong. Many native ponies running unshod on their natural terrain have this type of hard foot, but with a good, well-developed frog.

Club or mule feet are a more pronounced version of boxy feet, with an even greater angle to the ground.

Long or fleshy feet can be similar in some aspects to flat feet. The toe is long and cannot be reduced to normal size without risk of injury to the internal fleshy structures.

Thin soles are very sensitive soles.

Dropped soles are convex and in acute cases below the surface of the wall. Dropped soles are often a sign of chronic laminitis with rotation or sinking of the pedal bone.

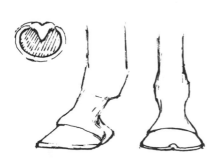

Flat feet.

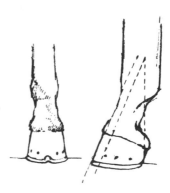

Boxy feet.

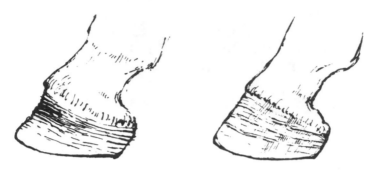

Rings and grooves on foot.

(*left*) Laminitis rings. (*right*) Diet rings.

Pronounced ridges or rings are a sign of an alteration of the growth rate. They can be caused by past or present disease, such as laminitis, or by incorrect hoof trimming. The rings are widely spaced at the heel and converge at the toe. Those associated with a change in diet run parallel to the coronet.

Brittle feet can be partly inherited or may be due to incorrect diet. Careless rasping of the wall, resulting in loss of moisture, or dry weather, resulting in the natural loss of moisture from the hoof without its being replaced, can be contributing factors. Careful balancing of the diet, regular exercise and skilled farriery may improve brittle feet.

CARE OF THE FEET

A horse turned out on good pasture, or a stabled horse on a balanced diet, should be receiving all the necessary vitamins and minerals for the production of strong horn. However, the metabolism of some horses is such that in spite of a suitable diet, they still have weak and brittle feet. Improvement can then be made by adding biotin, a member of the vitamin B complex, to the diet. Methionine, zinc, or glycerine are also useful additions and may help. Stable hygiene and the type of bed used is also important for the maintenance of strong feet.

Methods of Improving Horn Growth

☐ Regular attention from the farrier can improve the shape of the foot, and reduce the risk of damage to the wall by a lost shoe. Rasping of the wall must be minimal. The frog and sole should be trimmed, to remove untidy and dead fragments, but not cut back.

☐ Stimulating ointment rubbed daily into the coronary band encourages the growth of horn but will not improve texture. Care must be taken not to blister the coronet.

☐ Regular oiling of the wall will prevent undue evaporation, but too much oiling of the feet, particularly of the sole and coronary band, restricts the amount of moisture that the foot is able to absorb, and can cause brittle feet.

Unshod Horses and Ponies in Work

Horses who are ridden on soft surfaces, for example in a school, with little road exercise, can work without shoes. Ponies with naturally hard horn often work without shoes, although some may need shoeing in front, particularly if they work on rough or flinty surfaces.

In a dry season most horses'/ponies' feet are hard, and will stand up to wear, although some horses' feet in dry conditions lose moisture and become brittle. In a wet season the feet may absorb too much moisture, and the sole and horn become soft, thus making shoeing necessary.

When the shoes are first removed, the horse/pony may go a little short until the feet harden. If there is no improvement, then the horn texture is not standing up to work without shoes.

Horses/ponies in work without shoes will on occasions wear the feet down to a degree where they become foot sore. It may then be necessary to put on shoes and allow sufficient new horn to grow before removing them again.

An alternative is to rest the animal until the horn has grown, or to work on soft going only.

Care of unshod feet entails:

☐ Regular inspection of the feet, including removal of small flints and debris which may cause infection and lameness.

☐ Every four to six weeks the farrier should dress the feet to maintain their balance. Some animals wear the toe, some the heel area, and some wear more on one side than the other. It is important to level up the foot, and to give the animal a level bearing surface.

Horses at Grass and Not in Work
Animals with good strong horn growth should not require shoes. The feet should be dressed every four to six weeks so that the foot is not allowed to grow out of shape.

Some horses have poor horn growth and a tendency to flat soles. This type of animal is better kept shod in front. Shoes should be a lightweight pair of normal shoes. The farrier should replace them every four to five weeks.

In a dry year when there is little grass, and on a rough or flinty surface, horses can become foot sore and may need shoeing.

Young Horses
Young horses with foot and/or gait problems may have them considerably improved if their feet are looked after from an early age by a skilled farrier.

PARTS OF THE SHOE

The web refers to the width of the material from which the shoe is made.

The branch is the parts of the shoe from toe to heel.

The heel and toe are self-explanatory.

The quarter is the part of the hoof between the toe and the heel.

The bearing surface is the part of the shoe in contact with the foot.

Clips are drawn at the toe of the front shoe, and usually at the quarters of the hind shoe, although some ponies and cobs not used for fast work and jumping may have a toe clip on a hind shoe. The clips should be solid, but not larger than the thickness of the shoe, and rounded rather than diamond shaped. If a shoe becomes loose or dislodged, the horse often treads on the clip, which can cause a serious injury if it is sharp.

Permanently *raised heels* (*calkins* and *wedges*) on the shoes of horses working on hard surfaces dramatically reduce the weight-bearing area of the shoes and therefore apply extreme pressure to the foot at the point where it is raised. Studs or nails can be fitted at both heels but they should only be used if extra grip is absolutely necessary.

TYPES OF IRON

Plain is heavy, straight-edged, flat iron.

Concave iron has a wider foot-bearing surface than ground-bearing surface. This reduces suction and gives a lighter weight shoe, but it also reduces the ground-bearing surface.

Fullering is a groove made in the ground-bearing surface of the shoe. It provides secure bedding for the nails and a better foothold.

THE MOST COMMON TYPES OF SHOE

Plain stamped shoes are made of plain iron with nail holes stamped through the full thickness of the web. Both front

137

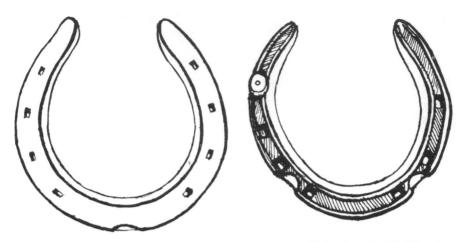

(*left*) Plain factory-made shoe for near or off foot. (*right*) Hunter shoe with road stud for near hind foot. Fullered and concave.

and hind shoes usually have one toe clip. These shoes are only suitable for horses doing slow work, as they give a less secure foothold, and are also likely to cause 'interference', such as brushing or overreaching.

Hunter shoes are suitable for most riding horses and ponies. They are made of fullered and concave iron, with dressed heels, and have one clip in the front shoes, two in the hind. The heels of the shoes dressed to the angle of the feet lessens the risk of their being pulled off by a tread. Two clips in the hind shoes allow the shoe to be 'set back', the front edge to be rounded off, and the inner edge bevelled, all of which lessens the risk of an overreach or of the shoe pulling across the foot when jumping and turning.

To give better grip, hind shoes may have a calkin and wedge heel, although it is now more usual to use road studs. It should be remembered that any raising of the heel can give a false angle to the foot, cause side-to-side imbalance and reduce the weight-bearing area of the shoe.

Rolled toes on hind shoes are used on horses who drag their toes. The front of the shoe is turned up to make a thick, wide toe. The two clips can still be drawn if required. Reinforced steel can be put in the toe to give longer wear.

On front shoes, rolled toes are used for horses with long toes who stumble, but if the foot is short and upright, they can increase the stumbling. The shoe is set back on the foot, and the toe surface is rounded off.

Aluminium shoes are lightweight shoes used for plating racehorses. They may also be put on show ponies and hacks. Plating is a term for shoeing horses with lightweight shoes for racing. They are usually removed the following day and replaced with normal exercise shoes.

Racing plates are lightweight steel or aluminium shoes for racehorses. They are often fitted without clips.

Various technical shoes, for example *bar shoes, branched shoes, grass tips* and *high-heeled shoes,* may be recommended in special circumstances; but since these are likely to interfere with the primary requirement of trimming and shoeing – that is, to establish or maintain lateral-to-medial and cranio-caudel balance – specialist advice should be sought.

SHOEING TERMINOLOGY

Forge Tools for Making or Reshaping the Shoe
The anvil should be sufficiently heavy to withstand the blows of a heavy hammer during the making and shaping of a shoe. The beak or pointed end provides a surface for shaping the shoe.

Fire tongs are long-handled tongs used to hold hot metal, so that it can be turned in the fire.

Shoe tongs have shorter handles and are used to hold a hot shoe on the anvil.

139

Shoeing

The turning hammer is a heavy hammer used to shape the shoe and to draw the clips.

The stamp is a punch used to make the nail holes. By altering the angle of the stamp, the nail holes are drawn in closer to the inner edge at the toe of the shoe where the horn is thicker. These are called 'coarse holes'. As the wall becomes thinner towards the heels, the nail holes are made near the outer edge and are called 'fine'.

The pritchel is a long steel punch used to finish the nail holes begun by the stamp. It is also used to hold the hot shoe against the foot.

Shoeing Tools for Preparing the Foot and Nailing the Shoe

The shoeing hammer is a lightweight hammer for driving in the nails. The curved claw at one end is designed to grip and easily twist off the point of the nail.

The buffer has a blunt chisel end for cutting clenches, and a point at the other end for punching out broken nails.

The rasp is a heavy, flat, steel file about 41cm (16in) in length. On one side it is coarse cut, and on the other fine cut. It is used to make a level surface for the shoe, and also to smooth off any rough edges of horn after the shoe has been fitted.

The drawing knife has a curved blade with a bent-over, very sharp end. It is used for cutting off ragged bits of horn, and to cut out the small piece of wall for the toe clip. It may also be used to cut away any diseased portions of the frog.

The searcher knife has a lighter blade than the drawing knife, and is used to search and open up a punctured foot.

The toeing knife has a short flat blade. It is used with

the shoeing hammer to help prepare and trim off the foot surface before finishing with the rasp. It is used for the same purpose as hoof parers, but usually on heavy horses.

Pincers are used to lever off the shoe, to remove nails and to assist in clenching up.

Hoof-cutting pincers have overlapping blades (one thick, one thin) and are used for trimming overgrown feet.

The tripod is a three-legged iron support, which the farrier may use to support the horse's foot when he is cutting the clenches, or when finishing the foot.

SHOEING

The average horse requires a new set of shoes, or must have his old shoes removed and replaced, every four to six weeks. The time interval depends on the growth rate of the feet of the individual horse, and how he wears his shoes. Horses who are heavy on their feet, and who do a lot of roadwork, may need new shoes every two weeks.

Indications that Re-shoeing is Necessary

A lost or loose shoe.

The shoes are thin, either all over, or in one part.

The clenches have risen.

The shoe or shoes have spread.

The foot is beginning to grow over the shoe, resulting in the heels of the shoes pressing into the seat of corn.

The wall of the foot has grown and the foot is unbalanced.

The Process of Shoeing

Before shoeing a new horse the farrier should study the

horse standing square in his old shoes, and then see him walked and trotted up, so that he can observe any abnormalities of action. When viewed from in front the long axis of the limb should be over the centre of the shoe. He should also check the old shoes for any uneven wear. This may have been caused by faulty conformation or by unsoundness, but it can also result from faults in the dressing of the foot or the fitting of the shoe. When the old shoes are removed, the horse should be observed standing unshod and walking.

To Remove a Shoe

1. The foot is held between the knees, and the clenches are opened, using the shoeing hammer and the sharp edge of the buffer. Risen clenches are easily cut; tight clenches require more skill. The corner of the buffer can be placed against the clench, but on no account should the buffer be driven into the wall to raise the clench. With a heavy horse, it may be easier to place the foot on a tripod when cutting clenches.

2. With the foot between the knees, the pincers are used to ease the shoe at each heel, and then round the toe. The shoe is removed by gripping it with the pincers at the toe, and pulling it backwards towards the frog. On occasions it is necessary to remove the nails individually. In this case the clenches are cut, the shoe is eased at the heels and the shoe is knocked back with the pincers. This pushes out the heads of the nails, which can then be removed with the pincers.

3. The old shoe should be put out of the way, with the nails hammered flat, or it may be taken to the fire so that the new shoes can be matched up. Any loose nails should immediately be picked up so that the horse cannot tread on them.

Preparation of the Foot
It is necessary to restore the balance of the foot, and to

prepare a level bearing for the new shoe. The farrier should look at the shape and angle of the foot when it is on the ground. When viewed from the side, the angle of the foot and pastern should be the same. The foot is then picked up to observe the bearing surface. In most cases it is necessary to remove more horn from the toe than from the heels. In normal circumstances, the foot is reduced with the rasp; first the sides and toes are done and then, if necessary, the heels. If there is excessive growth, it is taken off by using either the hoof cutter or the toeing knife. Any untidy pieces of sole or frog may be cut off but, apart from this, if they are in healthy condition, neither should be touched. After the final balancing of the foot, the horse should again be observed standing unshod.

Hot Shoeing
The prepared shoe is heated, shaped and then applied to the foot to check for fit and bearing. To avoid excessive burning of the foot, it should be at a dull heat, and should not be left against the foot longer than is necessary to ensure level bearing. It is then taken to the anvil, where any necessary adjustments are made. After a final check on the foot it is cooled in water.

Nailing On
Nails must be of a suitable size (no larger than the wall of the foot can absorb) and must fit into the fullering. The end of the nail is shaped so that when it is driven correctly it emerges about one-third of the way up the wall. It is usual to have three nails on the inside of the shoe and four on the outside. The shoe is nailed on first at either the toe or the heel, and then on alternate sides. If the foot is broken or weak, it is important that nails should only be driven into sound portions of horn. In this case it may be necessary to drive the nail higher in the wall than is normally desirable, and also to make sure that nail holes in the shoe are stamped, so that weak parts of the wall are avoided.

If a nail is driven too close to the sensitive tissue it

143

causes a nail bind. It must be withdrawn immediately. This mishap is unlikely to happen if the horse has strong, well-shaped feet. It can occur more easily if the horse has broken or brittle feet, when considerable skill is required to fix the shoe firmly. On occasions, the farrier may 'prick' the foot, that is drive a nail into the sensitive tissue. Often, when the nail is withdrawn, it shows traces of blood. The horse may not be lame at the time, but infection is likely to develop in the foot and to cause acute lameness within sixty to seventy-two hours. The wall is of equal thickness from the coronary band to the ground surface and therefore the height of the nail is not likely to cause lameness.

As each nail is hammered home, the point is either immediately twisted off, or bent over and twisted off later. The end of the nail now forms a clench. The closed pincers are held against the clench, and the nail hammered tight. This turns the clench over. The clenches are shaped with the rasp, and then hammered flat against the wall. The rasp is used to smooth off the clenches, and the edge of the wall, thus making it tidy and finishing the shoeing.

Cold Shoeing

Hot shoeing has been preferred to cold, but farriers without a portable forge may have to shoe cold, and as long as it is done correctly it is as good. In fact, more problems can occur with hot shoeing, from over-burning a shoe on the foot, burning a foot unlevel, burning an unlevel shoe on to a foot, etc.

Arrange for the farrier to see the horse, measure the feet and see if there are any particular problems. A skilled farrier who makes his own shoes can shoe cold very satisfactorily. However, in the case of factory-made shoes which arrive complete with nail holes, a less satisfactory fit is obtained. Because the nail holes are always in the same position, when the shoe is put on nails may well have to be driven into weak horn. This results in a less secure shoe.

To Measure a Foot

If it is necessary to let the farrier know the approximate size of the shoes, the foot is measured from toe to heel, and then across the widest part. Any broken or weak parts of the wall should also be mentioned. An alternative method is to place the foot on a piece of paper or cardboard and draw the outline.

WHAT TO LOOK FOR IN THE NEWLY SHOD FOOT

When the Foot is on the Ground

☐ The foot should be suitably reduced in length at both toe and heel. The line of the pastern should be continued by the foot until the shoe and the ground surface are reached, i.e. straight foot/pastern axis.

☐ The frog should be close to the ground.

☐ The clenches should be in line, well formed and bedded, and the correct distance up the wall. They should not have been driven into old nail holes.

☐ The place for the clip should be neatly cut and the clip rounded and well bedded.

☐ The wall should have been rasped only lightly, and not above the line of the clenches.

☐ The foot should be level on the ground.

When the Foot is Picked Up

☐ The shoe should fit the foot. There should be no dumping of the toe. The heels of the shoe should be the correct length, neither too long nor too short.

☐ The type of shoe and the weight of iron should be suitable both for the work the horse is doing, and for the size and shape of the foot.

☐ There should be no unnecessary paring of the sole or cutting of the frog.

- [ ] The foot should be evenly rasped down and the heels level, and not opened up by cutting the bars.

- [ ] No daylight should show between the shoe and the foot, particularly in the heel area.

- [ ] The nails should be of a suitable size and should have been well driven home, so that they do not project above the surface of the shoe.

- [ ] The correct number of nails should have been used, usually three on the inside and four on the outside.

- [ ] The horse should be sound when he is trotted up.

FAULTS IN SHOEING

Dumping. The shoe is set back, and is often too small. The toe of the foot is rasped off to make it fit the shoe. The rasping of the wall exposes the soft underlying layers, which then become brittle and will not hold the nails. The foot itself has a neat appearance, but the fault can be easily observed because the angle of the wall changes as it comes towards the shoe. The foot itself has a smaller bearing surface.

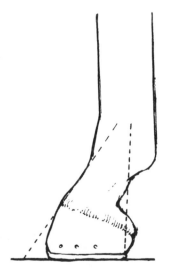

Dumped toe.

NB. Dumping of the toe should not be confused with rasping down the toe to obtain a normal hoof/pastern axis.

Over-lowering of the toes raises the heels and reduces the bearing surface. The angle of the wall on the ground is increased, and the balance of the foot, and therefore of the horse, is upset. Frog pressure is reduced and more weight is placed on the front of the foot. The heels should be one-third of the height of the toe from the coronary band.

Over-lowering of the heels puts weight on the back of the foot, with consequent extra strain on the tendons and ligaments. The angle of the wall to the ground is decreased, and the resultant long toe can cause stumbling, and the possibility of the development of navicular disease.

Opening the heels by cutting away the bars of the foot causes a weakening of the wall and of the heels, and results in contraction of the heels and in increased concussion.

Over-lowering of the bearing surface can occur through lack of judgement when a farrier first shoes a horse with flat, open feet. The bearing surface is rasped down too much and the horse becomes footsore. An uneven bearing surface occurs when one side of the foot is rasped away too much. When the foot is picked up and the shoe checked, the uneven surface can be seen. It can also result from a lost shoe, when one side of the foot is worn down or breaks off.

Rasping the walls results in the removal of the periople, and consequent drying out of the foot and brittleness. Ideally, rasping should be minimal, never above the clenches and only sufficient to finish and tidy the foot. However, in the case of long-toed feet, some extra use of the rasp is necessary.

Shoes too heavy may cause some form of interference, such as brushing, overreaching, etc. If the horn is not strong, a shoe may come off and often it will take a piece of the wall with it.

Nails too large may split and damage the wall. The resultant loss of holding power may cause problems when the horse is next shod. There is also a greater risk of nail binding. The head of the nail sits above the fullering, and thus receives more wear.

Excessive burning of the horn when applying a hot shoe to the foot. The shoe should be at no more than a dull red heat, and should be held in contact with the foot only for as long as is necessary. If it is subjected to too much heat, the wall surface is weakened and may well crumble away, leaving a loose shoe. More often, the interior soft tissues of the foot are affected by scalding.

Nail bind occurs when a nail is driven too close to the sensitive laminae and causes pressure. When the horse is trotted up after shoeing he goes unlevel or a 'little feeling'. The nail must be removed and another nail driven in at a less steep angle. This lameness can occur as long as seven to ten days after shoeing.

Nail prick is when a nail is mistakenly driven into the sensitive laminae. The horse shows pain, and the nail when removed may show traces of blood. Often, the horse trots up sound at the time, and may not go lame for two or three days, by which time pus will have formed in the wound. The shoe will have to be removed, the nail route traced and opened at the base, and the foot poulticed.

STUDS

The use of studs should be considered with extreme caution. They affect the angle at which the shod foot meets the ground, alter the bearing surface and balance of the foot, and increase the wear of the shoe at the toe. These problems can be resolved if the stud in an outer heel is balanced with a plug or set-up heel on the inside, and if the toe is thickened and reinforced with steel insets. In this way, the balance and angle of the foot can be maintained.

Studs are made from specially hardened steel, and are used to give a better foothold. Road studs are put in for slippery roads and jump studs for jumping.

Road studs can be hammered in and remain a permanent feature of the shoe. When the horse is re-shod, it is often possible to remove the studs from the old shoes and to use them again. They are usually placed on the outer heel of both hind shoes, but they may be put on the outside quarter of the shoe. For even greater security, they can be put on the front shoes, too, although this can cause greater concussion and the risk of tendon strain from steadying too abruptly. There is also a risk of treads if studs are placed on the inside heel.

The screw-in type of road stud can be used if it is necessary to replace it with a larger stud for jumping.

Jump studs come in several shapes and sizes. Generally, large square studs are used for deep mud, and smaller pointed studs for hard ground. The actual choice of stud is very much one of individual opinion, and must relate to ground conditions at the time.

On a narrow web shoe, it may be necessary to widen the shoe at the heel to give room for the stud holes, which are made when the shoe is hot. To ensure correct fitting, and because studs can vary, it is important to show the farrier the studs which you plan to use.

If the stud holes are not filled by road studs or plugs, they should be greased and packed with cotton wool. This ensures that they are kept clean and facilitates screwing in of studs at a competition.

Studs in a horse's shoe can result in an extra risk of injury to both horse and rider from a strike or kick. For this reason, studs are not permitted in racing. Their use for cross-country competitions must depend on the going and on local conditions. For dressage, again it depends on the conditions of the day. Studs can give more security to the horse on corners and in transitions, but on hard going they may shorten his stride and emphasise any unlevelness. The horse must be allowed to get used to working with studs.

Equipment Required for Fitting Studs

☐ Nail for removing cotton wool.

☐ Metal tap for cleaning out and reviving the thread of the screw hole.

☐ Spanner for removing and screwing in studs.

☐ Fresh oiled wool for placing in the holes when the studs are taken out.

☐ Screwdriver to fix or remove plugs, if used.

Drive-in Plugs
These can be more effective than studs on a slippery road surface and in snow and/or ice. They are fitted round the shoe, and therefore give an even bearing and do not upset the balance of the foot.

Pads
Leather or synthetic pads can be used, either temporarily to protect an injured sole, or on a permanent basis to minimise concussion and bruising in the case of horses with thin soles. Before a pad is fitted, the sole and frog should be treated with Stockholm tar and the sole padded with Gamgee or a similar material.

The synthetic pad is cheaper than leather, but because it is more likely to make the sole and frog sweat, it makes it more difficult to keep these structures healthy. A synthetic pad shaped to the shoe, and continued across the base of the frog, can ease concussion. The bar over the frog can alter the balance of the foot and care should be taken over this. Leather pads are also affected by conditions – when wet, they compress between the shoe and the foot, causing clenches to rise; when dry, they become rock hard. A more effective protection for bruised or thin soles, and one which minimises concussion, is a rubber or plastic cushion, which fits under the shoe but leaves the frog area clear.

Wedge-shaped pads can be used to ease the pressure on the tendons and to reduce concussion.

In snow or freezing conditions, pads fitted under the shoes help to prevent snow balling in the feet.

Bibliography

BRITISH HORSE SOCIETY, *Manual of Horsemanship* (Threshold Books).

CODRINGTON, *Know Your Horse* (J.A. Allen).

HICKMAN, PROFESSOR, FRCVS, *Stable Management* (Academic Press).

HOUGHTON-BROWN, J., AND POWELL SMITH, DR V., *Horse and Stable Management* (Granada Publishers Ltd).

ROSE, MARY, FBHS, *Horsemaster's Notebook* (Harrap).

TUKE, DIANA, *Horse by Horse* (J.A. Allen).

HMSO, *Animal Management.*

Horse and Hound Survey.

Index

Index